EMOTIONAL PROBLEMS OF ADOLESCENTS

Emotional

Problems

of ADOLESCENTS

J. Roswell Gallagher, M.D.

and Herbert I. Harris, M.D.

New York OXFORD UNIVERSITY PRESS 1958

© 1958 by Oxford University Press, Inc.
Library of Congress Catalogue Card Number: 58–11358

Second Printing 1959

To C. D. G. *and* E. W. H.

with deep gratitude

for their constant understanding and encouragement.

AN ACKNOWLEDGMENT

All physicians have a deep feeling of indebtedness to many people: their families, their teachers, their patients, and those benefactors who generously support hospitals and institutions of learning. We, the authors of a book which we trust will benefit young people, are, in addition, deeply grateful for the confidence expressed in us and the support given for many years by the founder, trustees, and officers of The Grant Foundation, Inc. Were it not for their sincere interest in helping young people to become happier, healthier, and more effective adults, and for their encouragement and the generous aid given us in our efforts, little of what we tried to do would have been accomplished.

J.R.G.
H.I.H.

FOREWORD

MOL AN ÓIGE AGUS TIOCFA SÍ
'Praise youth and it will prosper.'

This book has been written for all who deal with adolescents either in groups or individually. It is for parents, ministers, teachers, physicians, coaches, club and camp leaders — in short, for all who wish to know more about adolescents so that they can take a more active and a better informed part in helping them to become happier and more effective adults. By discussing adolescents' characteristics and their problems we both hope to furnish the kind of information and to develop the kind of attitudes that will enable adults to understand young people better. We do not believe that this book is too difficult or too frightening for the non-professional. In the first place we abhor jargon and we believe that matters which are well understood can be explained in simple language. In the second place we believe that the upset parent, minister, teacher, or other adult will gain equanimity and effectiveness in dealing with adolescents when his understanding replaces the fears and frustration that inevitably arise when one is unable to explain or to correct a difficult situation. We cannot believe that having this knowledge will increase anxiety.

Throughout this book emphasis will be put upon the fact that although adolescents have problems, the adolescent boy or girl is a *person*, not a *problem*. It is this individual, not the failure in school, the stealing, or the rebellion, who needs to be understood. We trust, too, that our readers will remember that many of the problems which plague both adolescents and the adults who deal with them are universal and are weathered by most adolescents without much assistance and with little damage.

Adolescents' emotional and behavioral problems baffle their parents more than they do other adults because there are such close ties between parents and their children that it is very difficult for them to be objective. At the same time, however, since many adults may readily slip into his parents' place in an adolescent's mind, these others may also experience all the bewildering vagaries of behavior which confuse and upset parents. So it is that teachers, ministers, or coaches may become involved in the adolescent's rebellion, crushes, thievery, or school failure. They, and other adults who can and do play such an important role in young people's lives and development, will be most helpful — and least likely to become uneasy and frustrated — when their insight into adolescents' behavior is based upon a knowledge of what young people are like.

That sort of knowledge we have tried to set down in this book in the hope that it will assist parents and others to prevent adolescents' problems from becoming incapacitating, reduce adults' bewilderment, and increase the effectiveness of adults' efforts to help young people to become mature citizens. We cannot give directions as to how this or that parent or other adult should 'change' in an effort to solve some boy's or girl's problem. The emotional ties are unique in every instance and are too varied, too involved, to justify any such opinions. Usually it is the adolescent's feeling which must change — it is he who must learn to adapt himself to things as they are. Often the most important gesture a parent can make is to remain steadfast and consistent so that as the adolescent strives to become an adult he feels that at home he has a solid and predictable, albeit not ideal, base. In short, it is not a question of parents and other adults learning to modify their *behavior* which is of primary importance: it is that they increase their *understanding* of young people.

As this book's title implies, it is about problems. While on the one hand we know that only a very small percentage of adolescents get into trouble, and that not more than 10 per cent are even briefly handicapped by the conflicts which arise as they progress from being children to being adults, on the other hand we are sure that a wider understanding of young people's needs and characteristics and of ways to prevent their more serious difficulties will come from a discussion of their problems. This is not to say that knowledge of these problems themselves is an unworthy goal, but rather that we feel it, in itself, is a limited one, and one not as rewarding as an effort to increase our understanding of each adolescent. One way that we can learn to do this is by trying to understand each one's problem: for here, in exaggerated form, are many of their minor and very common difficulties.

Adolescents *are* different. They are no longer little children, and they are only beginning to be adults. *They* differ from each of those; and *we* need to think differently about them when we try to understand them and their problems.

Their problems are different, too. If we had to name just three matters which confuse adolescents we would choose sex, loosening family ties and acquiring independence, and obtaining success and recognition from their own age group. Many other things bother them: failure in school, homesickness, fears, their own growth and maturation, religion, death, assuming adult responsibilities, and dissension at home. Each of these is important and brings its problem to many young people. Religion, for instance, which is a great source of strength and comfort to many during this growing-up period, is now questioned by others, who, struggling to build their own lives and beliefs, seem temporarily to need to suspect or discard everything their elders have handed down. It is ironical that at this time when they are most uncertain — and at a time when we encourage them to think for themselves — that some need to reject those religious beliefs and those people most likely to aid them to achieve maturity. The pastor, the rabbi, the priest, who understands all this, who is available, who listens with an equanimity we wish all adolescents to gain, is (though they vociferously deny their need for help) a source of great support to adolescents. The respect and esteem which generations of Yale men feel for their beloved Chaplain Sidney Lovett is, happily, but one of many examples of what religion and a man of religion can do for young people.

While adolescents are wrestling with religion and many other matters that constitute problems for them, while they are striving to become mature adults, they can be as confusing as they are confused. We hope, however, that by trying to make clear what is going on in the minds of those adolescents who have problems that all this will seem less unusual and bizarre, less chaotic and baffling.

Wisdom is the principal thing; therefore get wisdom: and with all thy getting, get understanding.

Proverbs IV–VII.

CONTENTS

EMOTIONAL PROBLEMS OF ADOLESCENTS

I

General Statement

The role of the adult is not to protect adolescents from all adversity and from every difficult experience. These they must meet and conquer if we are to develop calm, mature citizens able to meet the demands of adult life. But it *is* an adult's role to understand, to guide, and to give temporary assistance when a young person is faced with overwhelming odds.

We all need to know more about adolescents. They are, after all, the adults of tomorrow, the inheritors of our civilization. Those who are now handicapped, or whose personalties and future effectiveness and happiness are threatened, have still the hope of change for the better. Soon the malleability, that capacity for change, will be largely lost; for adolescence is the last of the age periods in which we can expect success from other than the most expert and the most prolonged efforts to strengthen personalities or to build emotional and physical health.

The importance of seizing this opportunity during adolescence cannot be stressed too strongly. This is the time to try to eliminate those incapacitating fears which still persist, to modify those feelings which hinder emotional growth, to foster the strengthening of conscience. These are still the adaptive, imitative, pliable years, but before long habits will become so fixed and feelings so deeply repressed that it will be many times more difficult to straighten them out.

It is not only those young people who bring troubles up from their early childhood into adolescence who now may need understanding help. So, too, do those who, previously well adjusted, now waver and threaten to succumb to the conflicts, confusion, and stresses which the normal changes and events of adolescence put upon them. Clearly, the better we understand these changes and stresses, and the better we understand the problems which beset all young people, the more effectively can we help them ourselves or help them to procure the proper sort of assistance.

Some adults intuitively say and do just the right thing that will tip the balance in a troubled adolescent's favor, while others, though better informed, may fail to be of assistance. This, however, does not mean that a greater knowledge of adolescents is of little value. It does mean that knowledge without *feeling* may be useless. These young people are not yet independent — they are only striving to be. How you *feel* toward them can be a greater factor than what you *know* about them. There is all the difference in the world between understanding *adolescence* and being genuinely interested in *an adolescent*.

But an adult who is interested in young people and feels sympathetic toward them will be able to do more for them as he acquires a greater knowledge of their traits and needs and problems. It is because we know that teachers, doctors, ministers, and camp and club directors have this real interest in adolescents that we direct this book to them as well as to parents. We hope that it will aid them in the tremendous part which they all play in young people's development.

As a basis for understanding adolescents one must know something of their physical characteristics. Admittedly, and this is important always to remember, they differ widely from one another, but they all follow the same general pattern of development and have for the most part similar needs and problems. One matter which is of great interest and concern to them, and which frequently effects their happiness and behavior, is the growth and development of their bodies. Therefore, a knowledge of the facts concerning growth and development during this age period is important. Any minor blemish or defect is regarded by the adolescent with much more interest and worry than it should cause. A supernumerary nipple, for instance, which is an interesting but insignificant finding as far as his physician is concerned, can be a source of considerable worry. At this stage of their emotional development nothing unusual about their bodies is insignificant or amusing to them: their appearance, which they formerly ignored, now keeps them before a mirror.

Little children and adults have slight emotional concern with their size. An eight-year-old child does not care how tall or mature he is, and a thirty-year-old adult does not become emotionally upset by the fact that his height is greater or lesser than his neighbor's. The adolescent, however, feels differently. Height, weight, and state of sexual maturity all mean a great deal to him. The adolescent who is not maturing as rapidly as his or her companions, the boy who is shorter, or the girl who is taller or more obese than usual, dislike being different and may become emotionally upset fearing that they will keep on getting taller or fatter or that they will never mature. Some of this overconcern with their own maturity and size is due to adolescents' conservatism, to their desire to be like their associates. Some of it arises out of the fact that both are factors in their athletics, in their social success, and in their acceptance by their own age group. Some of it develops because for years their parents, teachers, and physicians have expressed such great interest in their development and have compared them to charts and to standards which children accept unquestionably and yet fail to understand or actually misinterpret. At times their overconcern and anxiety arise because they imagine that their masturbation, in which they persist, may be adversely affecting them.

Few adolescents are aware that wide variation from the average is compatible with normality: to most of them to vary from what is average is to be abnormal. They need to understand the fact that a variety of different states and rates of growth and development are normal.

As their bodies develop and change, so do adolescents' interests and attitudes vary from those of their earlier years. When the adolescent was a baby, his crib measured the limits of his world. Next his playpen, later his back yard and his own home held all he had to understand. Then, a boy, he entered that wonderful carefree time of climbing fences, teasing girls, collecting everything, rising early, yelling, and chasing cats — a time of shyness, despising soap, stuffed pockets, and insatiable appetite. Now he is an adolescent. Soap and girls are no longer ignored, a trouser crease is more important than a bulging pocket, his ten thumbs and tripping feet show intermittent promise of coordination, he sleeps late, and only when off guard or with his group does he shout or let himself go. A tennis racket has replaced the slingshot, and football has replaced the raucous cops and robbers.

Those are the little changes. The major ones are their wanting to be grown up, their need for success, their striving for acceptance by their group and for prestige, their rebellion against authority, their negation of their families and their loyalty to their gangs, their idealism and their questioning of what they used to accept on faith, their interest in sex. And yet their striving, their interests and their rebellion vacillate. An adolescent will let his first 'glamorous date' wait while he shows a friend a new rifle, and he will fear at the end of a hard-fought struggle for independence to accept the freedom he has won. His sister, a grown-up party girl one night, tries to outswim her brother the next day.

Much of this turbulence of adolescence comes from their confusion as to which parent they should model their behavior on. It would seem a simple matter of boys following father, and girls their mother; but the fact is that this matter of being attached to and wanting to please and imitate the appropriate parent can be one of the more disturbing processes of adolescence. The implications are clear. A girl is more likely to want to grow up to be feminine and to take on the responsibilities of a wife and mother if her own mother is one she admires and is one whose happy life makes marriage seem a most desirable state. The boy whose friendly father goes at life with zest and pleasure is one who encourages a desire to grow up. When the opposite is true it should not be surprising to find a girl or boy preferring not to grow up and trying in a variety of ways to be unlike the parents.

If there is one single thing to remember about adolescents it is that they are overconcerned with their own personalities. They want passionately to be themselves. They are so preoccupied with developing their own personalities, so on guard against being pushed around, and yet so vacillating in the capacity to be themselves, that one cannot hope successfully to deal with them or to understand them unless one recognizes this preoccupation and pays as much attention to *them* as one does to whatever it is that one is trying to advise, to teach, or to correct. The adolescent is so aware of the need to develop himself — his own personality — that he instinctively resists any effort of yours to impose on him your will or your ways, though left alone he may imitate you. In short, an adolescent is more aware of his own personality than is a child, and less willing or able to sacrifice part of himself than is an adult. The wise teacher recognizes this and teaches, and shows interest in, each student, not just in history or mathematics. In like fashion the experienced physician treats his patient, not just the diabetes or the heart murmur. It is well to remember that adolescents are particularly responsive to anyone who is genuinely interested in them and their ideas. After all, they have had years of being told what to do, what is right, and little chance to state their own ideas without meeting quick criticism. The gains that can come from listening, from asking their opinion, and from avoiding preaching, sarcasm, and authoritarianism, are obvious. >

Gaining recognition and prestige, matters associated with sex, and acquiring independence are the three chief problems which face all adolescents. Boys — and many girls — in this age group go at things strenuously. They want success and recognition desperately, and moderation is not in their vocabulary. For this reason prescriptions involving rest and restriction should be avoided unless they are really warranted, and when given should be accompanied by patient, thorough explanations, and by an effort to provide compensatory activities. It is usually better to think of strengthening these young people so that activities will not fatigue or strain them than it is to restrict them or to suggest that rest will relieve their tiredness. Furthermore, in evaluating their fitness (of their hearts or knees or backs, for instance) it is well to remember the strenuous way in which they live.

Sex is one of their most baffling problems. They are physically mature, their sexual drive is at a high point, and they are confused by the difference between what is preached and what is practiced. Much of what magazines, movies, television, books, newspapers, and life around them portray contradicts their early training in home, church, and school, and yet is more in tune with their feelings. The facts, however, are that their emotions have not reached a level of maturity comparable to that of their bodies, and that their communities neither tolerate in them those activities which have been fictionalized and reported so glamorously nor wholly accept some of the substitutes which occur to them.

No less important to adolescents are their changing relationships to their parents. It is the time of breaking away from home, of trying to stand independently, of temporarily leaning on one's gang or club or sorority as they rely less on their parents and still hesitate to stand alone. Vacillating both in their desire and capacity to be independent, many of them behave in an awkward graceless fashion. Realizing that it is imperative that they learn to be independent, but apparently unaware of how dependent we are on one another and how essential cooperation is, neither they (nor their parents) behave in a consistent or pleasant manner. Often those who depreciate their parents most, and are most cruel to them, are the insecure ones who find the leaving of their parents the most difficult. It is as though only by denying how important their parents are to them can they bear to try to tear away. It can be a trying time for them — and equally so for an anxious, insecure, possessive parent who both fears for them and clings to them.

Rebellion is so common and what lies behind it so important that we must say a word in praise of this unpleasant phenomenon, this awkward nasty behavior of young people who find this stage in the transition from utter dependence to independence so difficult. We all should remind ourselves that conformity and dependency, though less apt to disturb the peace, may in reality promise only unhappiness and ineffectiveness for the days of adulthood which lie ahead.

The adolescent's imperative need to achieve independence cannot be overemphasized. As young people grow up, they should have increasing opportunities to try their own wings: these they now need as they formerly needed adults' constant protection and support. Now to continue to protect them, now continually to thwart their attempts to develop independence, is to rob them of the abilities, confidence, and resiliency they must have in the demanding and unpredictable adult world they face. They will make mistakes; they may not do as well alone as they could have done with help, but they must learn to do for themselves. Most of them instinctively realize this and rebel when these opportunities are denied them.

These, and such matters as death, religion, conflict between their parents, and fallen heroes are to be kept in mind when one is trying to understand an adolescent. By keeping them in mind, by remembering that these are the sort of things which confuse and upset them and lie behind much of their baffling behavior, we stand the best chance of helping them.

Realizing that these people are growing up and now have such matters as sex and acquiring recognition and independence very much on their minds, an adult's handling of, and relationship to, them will be very different from what it used to be. They are no longer just little people, to be scolded, to be told, to be protected. Now they are old enough increasingly to be encouraged to have opinions, to take responsibility, to make decisions. Having produced children, now we need to show confidence in them if we are really to help them to become men and women.

The more this can be done the better will adolescents co-operate — and the greater will be our contribution to their well-being. This does not mean that parents no longer play a role. They do, and a very important one — but it is a very different one from the role they played with the little child who primarily needed their protection and love. Now the adolescent needs to do for himself, and to feel that you are behind him, but not supporting him, advising him only when really necessary and confident of his improving judgment and of his ability *now* to profit from his inevitable mistakes. And yet at the same time that adults realize that their suggestions and warnings will be interpreted by the adolescent as evidence of little confidence in him and so increase his own anxiety and diminish his small store of confidence in himself, they also need to remember that striving for maturity isn't the same as having achieved it. Until adolescents are really confident and independent they like to feel that help and support will be forthcoming when needed. This new role for parents and other adults who deal with adolescents isn't always easy, but it isn't too mysterious or difficult if one will accept the fact that as these young people change our roles too must change.

To build confidence, to strengthen their egos, they need to be trusted and they need the happy experiences and the recognition which achievement and success bring. There are few adolescents who do not get their full measure of criticism and failure: almost all would benefit from more trust and praise and more success. The Irish have a wise saying: *Praise youth and it will prosper.*

We have been outlining some of the usual problems and characteristics of adolescents, the kind of changes and questions *which most of these young people face and conquer.* These are matters for many of us — not just for their parents — to remember, for during these years of beginning to be an adult and giving up being a child, which is what adolescence really is, young people are breaking away from their parents and turning away from home. So when parental impulses prompt one to try to help the adolescent to mature, such efforts may bring only rebuff and hurt feelings and bewilderment; but this also is the time when they may turn for help to other adults with whom there are no close emotional ties and little embarrassment. Given this advantage, the teacher, doctor, minister, coach, and club leader are in a favorable position to be of assistance.

We know but few of the answers. Unfortunately no one knows them all, but in this book we will try to help others to see through the transient vagaries and annoyances and inconsistencies of adolescents to their essential selves which lie underneath. We will discuss in detail some of the emotional disturbances which affect adolescents, but we want to emphasize that an acquaintance with these conditions is important chiefly because of the hints they give of ways to prevent similar but much less severe upsets.

There are few rules and few generalizations which will aid those adults who would help adolescents, and, valuable as it is, a wide knowledge of the dynamics of human behavior is not essential. But some facts, a thorough acquaintance with methods of going about helping young people, and a clear picture of one's objective, will make your genuine desire (which is the primary factor) to help the adolescent more effective and more rewarding.

II

Mental Health

This chapter might be called 'The Role of the Family, School and Club in Mental Health Defense.' It will serve to direct our thought to the many emotional forces which begin to affect adolescents at home, in school, in their scout troop or club. What kind of forces affect adolescents at home, in school and in the various groups of which they are members? Of one thing we can be sure: these forces all arise from the *people* with whom these adolescents deal. The qualities of these adults' personalities, their steadfastness, their fairness, their understanding, their leadership are tremendous factors in the adolescent's emotional development. The physical things young people need are seldom neglected, but the things which adults could say and do to foster their emotional development are too often overlooked.

Mental health is our cardinal problem. It disrupts more lives than does physical illness. Parents and teachers, who direct young people for many hours of their day, play a tremendous part in the prevention of mental illness and in the early detection of emotional disorders, and in the management of those everyday problems which are warnings of later trouble. Others to whom this book is directed are in touch with young people fewer hours, but they too play an important role. Though much of this chapter is directed to teachers, most of the comments apply equally to parents, the clergy, physicians, club leaders, and coaches.

Educators are agreed that teachers' primary function in this area is *preventive:* to keep young people mentally healthy. And they appreciate the importance of teachers' being as familiar with the principles of mental health as they are with the subject they are employed to teach. This philosophy is founded on the belief that it is the school's function not only to teach the 'three R's' but also by action and by example to help as many young people as possible to flourish and to master the art of good human relationships.

Few nowadays dispute the primary importance of developing well-balanced personalities or deny that to *teach a boy or girl* is more important than to *teach a subject,* but a few are skeptical of the part which the laity should play in the prevention of mental illness. However, the professionals — the physicians, the psychiatrists, and the psychologists — cannot alone solve our mental health problems. It is not just that the quantity of mental illness makes it more than specially trained personnel can handle; it is that the nature of the problem is such that all manner of people must learn to understand it if we are ever to reduce its enormous amount. All adults must learn more about its causes so that they will more quickly notice those problems which plague so many perfectly normal young people and which, when ignored or allowed to multiply, lead to distress or disaster. Many of these matters can be helped at home or in school in a friendly but well-informed fashion, and do not require the help of psychologists or psychiatrists. Specialists should be on hand to advise and to guide; they should need to care only for those more seriously upset.

An acquaintance with the principles of mental hygiene not only makes the teacher or parent or clergyman or club leader or physician or coach a potent ally in the fight against mental illness, but also strengthens the effectiveness of subject teaching itself. Although the teacher who perhaps unintentionally discourages young people, like the instructor who is said to have told Dick Button that he would never be a great figure skater, can at times be a stimulant to outstanding success, usually learning is best accomplished by encouragement and in a friendly, relaxed atmosphere. The boy who feels secure, who has good relationships both with parents and his teachers, learns best. A boy's 'I do my best in history; my teacher is terrific' is fortunately heard often and is a meaningful comment. The teacher who practices the elementary facts of mental hygiene can be expected to command respect and to make his pupils wish to please him.

A schoolroom, club, or home which is relaxed and friendly does not mean one in which boys and girls do as they please. Leadership is essential to an adolescent, and they need early to learn to distinguish between liberty and license. They don't want to be pushed around, but they need and like a firm, respected adult in charge. 'My math teacher? She's O.K.; she's strict but she knows her stuff, she's fair, and she really seems to want to help us to learn.' In their clubs they look to the director, in the troop to their scoutmaster, on the playing fields to their coaches, in their school to their principal and teachers for this leadership, but the leader must be capable, honest, just, and genuine. Young people quickly detect feigned interest: they can sense a 'phony' a mile away.

In other days, when large families were the rule, the father was the leader of the group. He plotted the course, sailed the ship, and stood off the threats to safety. The principal of a school stands in a comparable position: to a lesser degree attitudes of dependency upon him develop in both his faculty and students. Just as they resent and rebel against high-handedness in their father at home, and are made to feel insecure and anxious when he is weak and vacillating, so do boys and girls resent and rebel against what they consider invasion of their rights and prerogatives and show evidence of poor morale when they have little confidence in their teachers' or their club leaders' ability and judgment. The emotional ties, the rivalries, the struggles for affection and recognition resemble those in a home. They differ only in degree, being most intense in the boarding school, less glaring in a large day school from which everyone goes his way at nightfall, and minimal in the club which is visited only occasionally.

The emotional tone of the school is determined in part by the quality of its principal, but its total climate is to a large extent the sum of each classroom teacher's attitude toward his students. That climate clearly reveals the teacher's own emotional tensions and maturity. For example, a teacher who suffered much loss of attention from his parents when his baby brother or sister was born may appear harsh and very much the martinet with his pupils because of the long-buried envy and rivalry which he bottled up as a boy. These are deep and powerful emotions, even though they may have long since been all forgotten. Surges of repressed feeling may arise in those who face a class which revives memories of their early childhood jealousies and defeats.

An unhappy, sarcastic, upset teacher recalled an incident from her early life which illustrates that point. On returning home from her grandmother's, where she had stayed for three weeks when her baby brother was born, she rushed to her baby brother's crib, not with the curiosity one might expect, but in a truly savage wish to kill the infant. This old, unrequited rage festered in her unconscious far into her adult life, warping her attitudes toward men, her pupils, even toward her own child. It is not common to gather such dramatic evidence, yet we can be confident that similar though less extreme buried feelings influence the classroom behavior of some teachers and the daily actions of many adults.

Young people's reactions to such a teacher are as predictable as they are undesirable. Though competent, honest, and faithful, Sally's teacher could not seem to resist every opportunity to criticize her, to be sarcastic, to hold her up to ridicule. None of Sally's early, innocent efforts to please her brought praise. It is easy to understand later why Sally was saying, 'I won't study, I won't go to school, I hate her.' The teacher who is fearful and retaliatory will arouse a student's wholesome anger.

The interplay of personalities in the classroom is no less lively than in a home. In school there is a constant interaction between student and teacher, and a wide variation in the quality of that reaction from teacher to teacher. To some teachers the class seems to be a threatening monster, and to others a volcano needing only the slightest provocation for eruption.

Such was the case in a young instructor whose unconscious was filled with long-repressed hostility for a younger brother. His classroom manner was halting, tense, and painfully insecure. He would correct quiz papers with a very sharp pencil with which he would jab any mistakes he chanced to discover; later he admitted that it gave him a feeling of 'ha — I've got you.' In class his palms would sweat, his throat and mouth would become dry; and at night he occasionally dreamed of being chased by hordes of students. His anxiety stemmed from his fear that his students would discover his unconscious hatred of them and retaliate. Fortunately, after he had begun to understand his feelings, his relationship to students, his satisfaction and pleasure in his work, and his effectiveness as a teacher all improved strikingly.

The teacher who feels that his classes are like active volcanoes may prove to have been pretty much of a 'sissy' as a boy, one who lived in mortal terror of the 'roughnecks' in the neighborhood. Now a teacher, he finds that the boisterous, breezy attitudes of the aggressive young males in his classes revive his old terror of the rough boys who plagued him and filled him with dread when he was young.

An endless variety of early experiences, defeats, and disappointments play a part in determining a teacher's emotional reactions to students and so vitally affect his relationship with them. Envy of his brothers or sisters, an unhappy adolescence, a thwarted desire for another career, all these may provoke harsh behavior which they regret and fail to understand. On the other hand, a teacher predominantly influenced during his adolescence by his mother may show a feminine solicitude which provokes anxiety, for tenderness is not in the masculine tradition and can cause confusion and uneasiness in boys. On one occasion a student came to his doctor in a state bordering on panic: he was not eating, he was losing sleep, was unable to concentrate on his studies, and gave every appearance of a boy suffering from intense anxiety. As he talked more and more about his trouble, the name of one of his male teachers occurred with increasing frequency. Slowly he approached an awareness of the fact that this teacher's attentions and considerate treatment of him at first made him grateful but that later feelings had been awakened for the teacher which had some of the qualities of an adolescent's first love. Slowly the boy began to see that what had happened was that much of the love and devotion he had had for his mother had shifted to this teacher, and the homosexual implications in such a state were the roots of his anxiety. When he came to realize these emotional goings-on, it became relatively easy for him to distinguish between his mother and the mother-like male teacher and to regard the latter with relaxed objectivity.

Teachers are neither ogres nor saints; they are only very human, with the faults and virtues of us all. They are like all of us — rigid and flexible; tolerant and impatient; happy and maladjusted. Their behavior stems from their pasts and is determined in the classroom and in the world outside by their own inner security, and needs as much understanding as does that of parents or judges or doctors or carpenters. It is only because of their close relationship to, and their strong influence upon, young people that it is particularly essential that we and they see beneath the surface aspects of their behavior to its motivating springs.

The understanding teacher regards his class as a group of individual personalities, growing and developing as they alternately agree and disagree with him and with each other. He is not afraid to build rich relationships with his students, encourages disagreement and debate; he makes no claim to omniscience; he regards the approach of each new student to his subject as a new personality whose acquaintance he is about to make. In short, he teaches boys and girls, not just history or science.

Teachers' attitudes and behavior are of more influence in forming a student's taste or distaste for education than are the subjects they teach. There is truth in the cynical warning that teachers must at all cost avoid destroying a love of learning. However, it is no more important to remember that teachers exhibit human frailties than to remember the remarkable resiliency of the adolescent. For centuries boys and girls have withstood the thrusts of many unhappy adult personalities, and yet each generation has produced its crop of scholars, scientists, and lovers of the arts. But even so, in these days of multiple pressures and in the face of the astronomical height of mental illness, our world's desperate need for learning, and our world's need for emotionally well-balanced adults, it is essential that thought and attention be given to every force, whether friendly or inimical, that bears upon emotional health.

One of the by-products of efforts to understand young people's personalities is the light it sheds on the idiosyncracies and tensions of those of our older acquaintances who behave in an immature fashion. It is obvious that all that has been said applies equally to all adults, to parents, club leaders, physicians, and coaches. The teacher is but one, though very important, of the forces affecting young people's mental health. Few adults are privileged to have the satisfaction which is the lot of that large group of teachers who are truly admired and respected by successive generations of students. Though an adolescent's praise is usually laconic and colloquial, it is no less heart-warming to have a boy or girl tell you his teacher is 'terrific.'

Teachers, though they usually teach groups, often of course talk to individuals; but it is mostly parents, ministers, physicians, counselors, and club leaders who talk to boys and girls alone. For all, the art of conversation is the *sine qua non* of success. It can gradually be acquired by anyone who really wishes to use it, and as it becomes a part of his personality it will become an art. Time after time someone will ask, 'How do you talk to an adolescent boy or girl? I never know what to say.' The answer, if not the practice, is very simple. 'Don't talk — listen.' Somehow it seems to be more difficult to learn to listen than it is to learn to talk; but how to listen, how to keep one's talking to a minimum, is a priceless asset.

Adolescents have had years of listening, years of hearing what parents, teachers, society, and the books say. Their doubts, their feelings, their questions, and their opinions yearn for expression. They have had a surfeit of listening — they want and need to talk. Often a parent who wants to tell a boy's story for him will say, 'Well, talk to him if you want to, but you won't get anything out of him. He never says anything.' When a good listener hears such a remark, he instinctively plans to allow at least an hour for his visit with the boy. The trouble will not be how to get him to talk but how to find time enough to listen to all he wants, and needs, to say.

Conversation is of course more than just listening; but listening is so much more effective than preaching, and the boy's telling you is so much more valuable than your telling him, that its importance cannot be overemphasized. To have him put his thoughts and feelings into words is all-important: what he says is secondary. The *feeling* he puts into his words is what counts. You should be interested in him and in hearing what he has to say, and you should be reluctant to advise or to tell him about yourself. What to ask, what to say, when to say nothing are things one gradually learns.

The quality of leadership and the interplay of personality forces which adolescents meet in school and club and church and home are two important factors in their development. A third is their ability and opportunity to express their emotions. We tend to forget the power and connotations which words have for our emotional well-being. For us to be more aware of the significance of the associations which color our reactions to many words would be a major contribution toward the prevention and amelioration of emotional disorders. Words are not only a means of communicating our needs and ideas; they are also a very important means of conveying our own feelings and evoking the feelings of others. The relationship of the spoken word to mental health becomes clear when one recalls the origins of neurotic behavior.

Disordered feeling or emotion is the basis of all neurotic disturbance. In the neuroses the emotions appear to have been upset because the sufferer has never put into words his fears and hatreds and loves. When these have neither been requited nor expressed verbally, they must find another outlet for expression; and so, instead of losing their force in speech, they flow out through one of the outlets of the sympathetic nervous system, whose language is a headache, indigestion, diarrhea, backache, or one or another of a host of bodily symptoms. A careful diagnostic search will fail to reveal any tangible basis for these headaches, backaches, or other symptoms, but they are no less uncomfortable and real, although their origin is emotional. Vomiting because your school or sister or boss makes you sick is just as real as the vomiting which results from the irritation of an ulcer. Unfortunately the expression of one's emotions by way of the sympathetic nervous system is no more than a bodily symptom; it gives no lasting relief. This type of expression is only evidence of the repressed emotions; it is *not* a satisfactory and requiting outlet for them.

These feelings, if they are really to be relieved and to lose their threat to one's physical and mental health, must be put into words. So the primary goal of the treatment of a neurosis is no more, and no less, than to put these feelings into words and thereby achieve an understanding of their nature and of their relationship to the present symptoms and behavior. When this is done, energy will no longer be used to repress these confused and powerful feelings and they will no longer need to be expressed as symptoms through the sympathetic nervous system.

These psychosomatic symptoms will be discussed in more detail in another chapter. Here we wish only to indicate how a knowledge of their origin and causes can profitably be used in the classroom and the club for the purpose of preventing their development. Exercises which freely use speech such as student dramatics, discussions, and debates have tremendous value for young people's mental health.

Opportunities given the adolescent to express his own feelings are often meager. Those few are further limited by the relative inability many adolescents have to express themselves in speech. This inability may well contribute to their need to *act out* their feelings. When youngsters drive cars in an utterly wild and daredevil fashion we may well ask ourselves 'What are they trying to *say* by this behavior?' The chances are that most of them are trying to say several things at once. Boys, especially, are trying to say, 'See how unlike my mother I am! I'm brave and daring and tough and all male!' Girls, on the other hand, may be trying to say, 'Even though I'm not a man, I can take it as well as they can!' Were they able to say these attitudes in words — and to understand them — their need to act them out could be much less.

By giving adolescents every legitimate opportunity to express feelings of which they are clamoring to be relieved, their emotional health will be happily safeguarded, and yet there need be little interference with the club or school program. Those schools where the teacher acts as a listener, encouraging spontaneous comments from the students in open classroom discussion, debates, and dramatics, are said to be producing very desirable changes in young people's behavior. Topics should be chosen which will encourage thinking and feeling in areas of strong emotion so that students are led to talk about their fears, hatreds, and loves.

This sort of classroom technique does not produce little brave-new-world creatures. On the contrary it promotes the development of every pupil's individuality. Nor will it, as some adults fear, destroy those forces which push one on into truly great creative work. There is little basis in fact for the opinion that by freeing people of their hates and fears, they will lose the source of their genius. The source of genius lies not in the tortured areas of a man's being, but in the force for life and creation that tries to push outward to expression. The objective is to clear the inner channels in a boy or girl so that this force will be able to flow out with as little impediment as possible. Many creative artists have times when they accomplish much and times which are periods of little accomplishment and discouragement; but once having rid themselves of the inner blocks to their own creative forces, such artists may be expected to reach high levels of activity which they can sustain for much longer periods.

The importance of the spoken word to mental health must not be confused with other types of expression. Other means of expression can serve as outlets for those feelings that are not widely accepted by society. In the graphic arts, for example, feelings that would be censured if written or spoken can be acceptably expressed in sculpture and painting. Music, as Hitschmann pointed out, is the most effective of all the arts in expressing feelings which society would not tolerate if expressed in words. But although the arts provide avenues for the relief of inner tension, they are not a complete substitute for the spoken word. They fail to increase one's self-awareness and self-acceptance. It is not enough to express feeling: one must understand these feelings and their relationships to one's thoughts and behavior.

Nor are such activities as the dance or athletics, which provide splendid outlets for aggressive impulses, as effective in promoting emotional stability and maturity as is speech. These activities are comparable to what is called acting out in the treatment of emotional disorders. In acting out, the patient regresses to childlike action to express impulses he is unable to put into words. The boy who smashes his schoolroom window or hurls eggs at his blackboard is saying by his actions things which are too violent for him to say in words.

When encouraged, speaking out one's feelings will do much for young people's mental health. It is obviously well within the power of any teacher or club leader and the scope of any curriculum to furnish many such opportunities. The rewards to all concerned will be rich. To the boy or girl will come poise and inner security and progress toward emotional maturity, and to the teacher will come new insights into his own personality and a heightened awareness of the behavioral meanings of his students and friends.

When we consider the means now at our disposal to help a boy or girl through the tensions and anxieties which not only their age but also modern living brings upon them, we find an embarrassment of riches. It is not that we know so little about adolescents and mental health which is regrettable; it is that we are so inconsistent in applying what we know. Admittedly our knowledge of personality is far from complete, but so is our knowledge of the many other sciences which we use with little hesitation. These few comments about leadership, about the interplay of personalities within groups, about words and expressing emotion, and about conversation indicate the factors which contribute to an effective and healthy emotional environment and ways in which one can play an important role in the defense against mental illness.

It is particularly important that those who live most closely to adolescents understand that as they develop emotionally, these young people return to their childhood levels over and over again. In adolescence time and time again they go rapidly and superficially through behavior reminiscent of their infancy and early childhood, so it is especially helpful for them to have the benefit of teachers whose understanding and interests are similar to those which would be ideal in a family. The adolescent's intermittent reproduction of childish behavior requires a great deal of tolerance, patience, and understanding, but its proper handling in these years can now make amends for mismanagement in the early years.

We all know how frequently and unpredictably adolescents vacillate between being quite grown up and very childish; how they hark back to the emotional patterns of childhood is clearly evident in their streaks of narcissism, in their total absorption in themselves, and in their lack of concern for others. A fourteen-year-old girl spends hours before the mirror doing nothing, or so it seems to others, but looking at herself from various angles. Her year-older brother, who recently ignored combs and clothes, must now have the prevailing style of haircut, sweater, slacks, and jacket, and studiously avoids anything which lacks his group's approval. They would not welcome the comment that all this is related to an infant's seemingly endless preoccupation with his toes!

Such adolescent self-love is hard to live with. This is an unpleasant time and state of mind, and it is easy to understand why all of us are prone to forget our own experiences and to reject the idea that we ever went through a like period. Impatience with their self-absorption, however, will do little to speed them out of it, but by emphasizing their mature deeds and by treating them as if they were adults, we can help adolescents through this uneasy time. Constant reference to their childishness does nothing except to perpetuate it. Finding some adult bit of behavior or some grown-up activity worthy of praise, and letting the boy or girl know that we recognize and approve is a powerful help at this time. They need recognition and acceptance. They need to be thought of as trying to become adults. Their attempts to grow up, even though awkward, need the warmth of praise, not the cold water of sarcasm.

In talking to adolescents in the classroom or office or home, an adult can make many mistakes and more rarely have brilliant successes. But if adults, whatever their capacity, can keep constantly in mind the truly deep need that youth has for recognition and for acceptance of themselves as adults, their successes will increase and their mistakes will become few. Adolescents are often tense and anxious when talking to an adult, and their anxiety may well cause them to fall back upon some mannerism or way of behaving, such as wiggling or twisting a sock, that they found useful in childhood but which is no longer appropriate. This behavior will embarrass them and increase their tension, and here it is best to ignore these aberrations tactfully and to proceed as if one were talking with an adult who was baffled and troubled and wants help although his pride is against asking for it. Such handling will win the majority of adolescents; from then on they will be ready to approach their difficulty with surprising awareness and good sense. It is important, too, to remember that a spirited and apparently unruly youth may have more potentialities, once these spirits are properly directed, than does the 'good' boy. The quiet, obsequious young boy or girl often has more of a personality problem than one who occasionally kicks over the traces.

The serious disorders of feeling which appear in adolescence require psychotherapy. Clearly it is much more efficient to exert our energy to try to prevent these troubles. This can be done by all interested and discerning adults who are closely associated with adolescents. What is needed is sympathy, the will to help, a belief in the primary importance of mental health, and a knowledge of the elementary principles of mental hygiene. Given these, a parent, teacher, club leader, or other adult can play an important part in keeping these young people healthy in mind and more effective in their jobs and studies. When a school or club or home has good leadership, morale will be good. There will not be widespread undercurrents of anxiety and insecurity when there is a capable and respected hand at the helm, and there will not be outbursts of resentment and aggression when the leadership is strong but not arbitrary.

Adolescents know when an adult is interested in them and when they are welcomed, not just tolerated. Unfortunately all of us know many adolescents who are ill behaved and doing poorly in school, whose parents protest that they have given them everything. They are baffled by their children's ingratitude, and insist that good old-fashioned discipline is what they need. Too often it is only *things* — food, shelter, toys, education, clothes, travel — that they have been given. Too often their emotions have been starved, and they have been given little opportunity to develop their own personalities and to express their own doubts and fears and feelings; had they been, their chances of becoming healthy, happy citizens would be increased many times.

III

Sex

Sex, mainly because of the taboos and restrictions of modern society, presents a dilemma to the adolescent. It is one of their major problems. Society prohibits full expression of hetero-sexuality and condemns masturbation, to which they uncon-sciously turned in early childhood, and does not fully approve the 'petting' of their later years.

Practically every adolescent youth faced with the imperi-ous demands of the procreative drive meets with anxiety. Either he finds himself uneasy and bewildered over nocturnal emissions ('nocturnal pollutions' the sex advertisements call them, thereby adding to the guilt surrounding sex); or he has recourse occasionally or frequently to masturbation and develops some degree of guilt over this overemphasized but fundamentally harmless activity.

Mature sexual expression is the goal, and during these trying, compromising, impulsive years the adolescent needs the good example and guidance of understanding adults. It is just as important that all things sexual not be tinged with guilt and indecency in his mind as that he restrain himself from entanglements which would overtax his emotional stability and capacity for responsibility. He is most likely to reach a satisfactory solution if he can see this problem for exactly what it is: a compromise which gives the fullest possible attention to the mental health and happiness of others as well as to himself, and at the same time meets the demands of the society in which he lives.

The advertising pages of some periodicals still print material which strikes fear in the hearts of confused adolescents. Fortunately, these publications (which mention masturbation, nocturnal emissions and 'sexual strains' in terms of mystery and foreboding) are far fewer in number today than they were twenty-five years ago. But uncertain adolescents who read such statements are apt to refer them all, with the intense self-consciousness of adolescence, to themselves.

Old wives' tales of man's sexual life die hard. It is not surprising that they do, for adolescents, lacking information and embarrassed to ask, are as likely to accept the false as the true. Even today we find college students who are guilt-ridden and lowered in overall effectiveness because of their persisting struggles with masturbation. This process, common to animals and openly practiced by children in simpler cultures than ours, can severely disturb misinformed and guilty adolescents. But after they have had a chance to ask questions and be reassured about the nature of this practice, the sense of relief they feel and the change in their entire behavior can be dramatic. However, many parents hesitate to talk freely of sexual matters to their children. When adolescents are denied this opportunity, some well-qualified person should provide them with both proper facts and proper attitudes.

A study of the origins of masturbation is revealing. Greatly accentuated by the development of the secondary sexual elements in adolescence, it represents another of the many regressive forms of behavior common to these years. In boys the regression in this case is to the old, intense attachment to the mother which so strongly colored his behavior in his early years. One of the most important concepts for those who would understand adolescent boys is the struggle which goes on in them between their need to emulate their fathers and become predominantly masculine *and* their impulse to cling to the femininity of their mothers. They are torn between the desire to be masculine and the unspoken fears that threaten their efforts to take upon themselves a man's behavior, activities, and responsibilities.

In girls' development masturbatory activity is less frequent than it is in that of boys. When similarity to the mother has been accepted and the drive to be like her grows, the girl appears to direct her attention and feelings toward her whole body rather than to the genital area. Hence, at this period, her interest in dress, hair ribbons, and dolls and their clothing increases. Girls who masturbate may have difficulty in developing the wish to be like their mothers, and among them will be found the tomboys who compete with boys and who seem to be saying by their aggressive behavior, 'I am just as powerful if not more so than you.'

The conflicts of masturbation should be solved no later than adolescence. If they are not, the adolescent's life pattern may be distorted and their proneness to neurotic disturbances greater as they tend to behave more like the parent of the opposite sex. Here is a time and place where an interested and informed adult can exert a powerful influence for sound emotional health and maturation. A few talks with an understanding physician or other well-informed adult can alter dramatically the behavior of a boy or girl who has been troubled by masturbation. While they will thereafter doubtless continue the practice sporadically, the release of emotional tension the talks effect usually results in a striking change in its frequency and its compulsive quality. Formerly preoccupied by fancied ills that might assail them because of what they believe to be a 'vicious habit,' they found it almost impossible to stop their thinking about masturbation, and this in turn almost inevitably led to their more persistent practice of it. Such preoccupation lowers many an adolescent's efficiency and leads to a very upset state of mind.

Masturbation is common and widespread among the youth of the world, though in some cultures it may be less widespread because of the earlier engagement in adult heterosexual activity which those societies permit. No physical ill effects result from masturbation, but emotional ills develop when the practice arouses guilt or fear. Although feeling guilty, the boy or girl persists in the habit and so becomes increasingly anxious and worried. When there is fear that some personal harm is being done, a kind of auto-suggestion takes place: masturbation is accompanied with the thought, 'I am hurting myself.' Instead of deriving erotic pleasure from the act, now expression is being given to unconscious needs to harm themselves. These use masturbation as a punishment, or more rarely as a means of making themselves physically less manly or less womanly.

The likelihood that masturbation persistently represents a desire to make oneself like a member of the opposite sex is uncommon, but it apparently exists in a modified form in some young people. The deep urge to be like the mother a son loves is not easily resolved. This is especially true when not to become a man would mean relief from the threat of resembling a father whom he dislikes. So, too, may arise the daughter's deep desire to be like her father and to escape being like her mother and to escape womanhood. At this time a boy is breaking with the urge to be like his mother, a girl with the urge to be like her father. The less a boy leans toward his own sex, the more will a boy feel himself a woman, and may behave so toward other boys with whom he is intimately associated. The less a girl leans toward her own sex, the more she will act like a boy and avoid things feminine. When their development stops here, some youths may drift into homosexuality with the grave unhappiness that this grossly immature disorder so commonly produces.

To busy themselves with other activities which occupy their time and bring them prestige and acceptance will help many young people during this period when they are adjusting their feelings to, and learning to live smoothly with, their new drives and relationships. This is not to say that these problems can be solved by immersing oneself in a ceaseless round of activity, whether it be social, academic, or athletic, but to occupy one's mind with satisfying and acceptable pursuits is clearly healthier than a guilty preoccupation with sex.

So we have here some facts for the anxious boy or girl or parent. Masturbation itself is harmless. It becomes a source of worry, however, in those who believe it harmful, persist in it, and therefore feel guilty. It may be a reflection of that adolescent's confused state of mind who finds it difficult to grow up to be like the parent of the same sex. Opportunities to get authentic information, to ask questions, and to talk out worries will help the former. More extended effort, perhaps professional help, opportunities to build a friendly and admiring relationship to an adult one would like to emulate,

as well as achievements which bring praise from one's contemporaries of the same sex will be needed to straighten out
the latter.

The chronological age at which boys become physically mature varies greatly. Some at fourteen are capable of reproduction; others show little evidence of secondary sex characteristics at sixteen. Consequently it is reasonable to expect considerable variation within a group of adolescents of the same
age in their heterosexual interests and impulses. The aggression, the power of the sexual urges, and the preoccupation
with sex evident in a boy who has matured early may lead
him to sexual intercourse while such behavior is beyond the
thoughts, the desires, and the capacity of his contemporaries
who are less mature. For the most part, adolescents' heterosexual experiences are fragmentary and sporadic, and less frequent in those whose interests and economic status permit
them to remain in school than in youths of the same age who
have taken their place in the workaday world. Adolescents less
fortunate economically or intellectually may use this way of
acting the adult to compensate for their scholastic shortcomings.

Several forces deter the adolescent from heterosexual activity. For the boy, the tie to his mother and his unconscious
fear of his father are important factors. Their attachment to
their mothers cause many to approach all girls as symbols of
their mother and consequently taboo. Even more profound as
a deterrent is the self-love or narcissism of the adolescent who
tends to regard everything about himself as perfect and not to
be defiled; so much has sexuality been associated with the
body's excreta in our culture that many youngsters regard activity associated with the genitals as unclean.

Then, too, the mores of our society restrain the adolescent
from sexual activity. All religious attitudes frown on too early

practice of adult sexual behavior. Since much of our religious formulation has grown out of the experience of the race, it is likely that this restraint has its roots in sound hygiene. It is well known that children of very young couples rarely show the vitality and intelligence of those from fully mature parents.

Counter to these forces are many ways in which the sexual motive is exploited. Most obvious of these is the erotic note in advertising. 'Cheesecake' is used to sell every kind of commodity: these advertisements imply that ravishing females such as those illustrated will fall into the reader's arms if he possesses the product advertised; their encouragement of adolescents' erotic daydreams is not likely to diminish the impulse to experiment with sex. The movies, too, bombard them with sexual innuendo. They use a device that Greek dramatists employed most effectively — by having the sexual act occur off stage, it is clothed with daydream unreality and added to the adolescent's already overstocked phantasy life.

Since rebellion against authority is so much a part of adolescence, and efforts to break the ties of dependence on parents are so perennial, parents' admonitions and forbidding attitudes about sex often stimulate the desire to disobey or ignore them. Much as the small child, during the period of testing his own powers says 'No!' to everything said to him, adolescents deny the worth of adults' attitudes. By the time a youth, boy or girl, has reached adolescence, each has learned many ways of saying 'No' to parents and other adults; and some, beneath apparent compliance and docility, break out into the most unbridled kind of behavior whenever the opportunity offers. Nothing really vicious need be present in such activity; it is more a graceless throwing off of the parental yoke. Adolescents, knowing little about sex, may, if their parents have failed to be frank and wholesome in their treatment of the subject, use clandestine experimentation as a means of expressing their rebellion.

Adolescents feel the need to copy grown-up behavior in every way possible. By doing things adults do they feel more grown up themselves. Smoking, drinking, and heterosexual activity, as well as staying up late and having a job and leaving school, to them represent being grown up. There is, too, what they consider the mark of manhood as an accompaniment of sexual experience. When in the throes of a struggle with the masculine-feminine elements in his make-up, or fighting for social acceptance by more mature and popular boys than he, a sexual experience is not so much a goal in itself as a means to an end. It, he thinks, will serve to prove his masculinity to his doubting self and gain him acceptance from those who have not admitted him to their circle. The need for acceptance on the part of the adolescent is so intense that it is very difficult to reason a boy or girl out of such a deliberate set toward sexual experience unless one can engage his or her feelings of regard to such an extent that the speaker's opinion really registers as coming from one admired, one who is, in a sense, a hero. Once having won the esteem of an adolescent it is not very difficult to point out the fact of the importance of a true love relationship on a grown-up level — a relationship which demands a deep and sincere involvement and sharing, totally unrelated to the transitory spasms of the sexual act of a frightened and tense adolescent. Properly described and emphasized it can become relatively easy for the adolescent who is threatened with sexual relations to resume the idealism which marked his entry into adolescence. This idealism, incidentally, has given rise to much of the idealism in our whole cultural tradition.

A more effective way of handling the problems of sex than by admonition, threat, or attempt to invoke fear is to treat the entire subject frankly and openly whenever it arises. Instruction in sex should begin when the child is little, and be given in small amounts; they want only simple, brief answers. It should not be deferred for one long, momentous 'talk.' Detailed discussions are not necessary. Adolescents do need, however, much more than some facts about anatomy and physiology. They need even more to know the social implications of sex, its part in family life. Their attitude toward sex is more important than a knowledge of anatomical facts. When mystery is removed from sex and an effort made to free it from its association with bodily excreta, and when they learn by personal experience within their own and others' families its part in happy family life, we can trust the idealistic adolescent to behave in an emotionally sound manner toward it.

Most parents nowadays find the discussion of sex with their offspring difficult, for they are, for the most part, emotional products of the traditions of the Victorian era. Those attitudes toward sex die hard. Today we have a conflict with that thinking: contrary attitudes have developed out of the new psychology, out of the mixture of people which was part of the first World War, and out of the extension of horizons which modern transportation has brought. Partly for these reasons and partly because 'sexologists' and psychiatrists have moved in different orbits and have failed to join their knowledge, a sound, broad view of sexuality is too rarely found.

It is most important for all adults who deal with adolescents to have themselves a mature attitude toward sex. The healthy sexuality of an emotionally mature person contrasts sharply with that of the emotionally childish one. The mature person is in control of this powerful force; the immature one, although seeming to be effective, is preoccupied by sex, not master of it. Mature sexuality embodies, in addition to the powerful physical urges that are necessary for man's survival, many factors which derive from our early emotional experiences. These are such as the forming of ties with people and things about us. As we grow up, the strong ties of our infancy and early childhood for our parents lessen and make more and more emotion available for forming bonds with other people. Later, when a lover is found, a mature person has more than his experience with mother or father or sibling love to call upon. He or she has also the contribution of the less selfish ties of many friends and associates. When this is true, mature love and marriage become the ideal experience that poetry and the arts express.

In contrast, the emotionally immature person, while maturing physically, has been unable to leave behind the impulses of infancy and childhood. The sexually promiscuous person, for example, is often one who has never given up his childish attachment to his mother. Such an attachment is accompanied by strong desires to be feminine like her, urges whose fulfillment is intolerable in a male society whose mores all conspire to frown on the slightest suggestion of femininity. Driven by these forces, and unaware of their nature, he strives desperately to prove his masculinity by what he considers a virile form of behavior — promiscuity.

Promiscuity is not common in adolescents, but the example of promiscuity given above is paralleled by some adolescents' behavior. During adolescence boys and girls are shedding the need to be like the parent of the opposite sex. This is a process that is continuously going on; it is not an accomplished fact at a given age. Adolescence is a particularly crucial time because if change is not largely accomplished during these years, the attachment to the parent of the opposite sex may become so fixed that the adolescent will find it most difficult, if not impossible, in later life to play the part of father or mother, husband or wife in a wholesome, emotionally mature manner. Their unresolved conflict over their sexual role is accompanied by other immature patterns of behavior which usually make both a marriage and its offspring unhappy and full of tension. Fortunately most boys and girls welcome the recognition of their need to be more masculine or feminine and value highly any effort designed to encourage its satisfaction. Schools which have an active and popular social program and which encourage the younger as well as the older students are a real help to adolescents in this regard. So, too, are small discussion groups, led by an understanding adult, which provide young people with a chance to express a disquieting conflict and to discover that their problems are not unique.

Several factors clearly affect premature heterosexual experience. In the first place there is the commendable restraint which develops out of a normal attachment to one's parents and therefore the symbols which they represent. Next there is the unfortunate deterrent which arises from the association of things sexual with things unclean — the result of poor or little sex education. Operating against these restraints are such forces as advertisements and movies, which keep sex in the forefront of adolescents' minds, and the adolescent's need to prove to himself that he has grown up. Little can be done about the former, but the latter can be met by treating the adolescent as if he had grown up, by encouraging other activities which might give him prestige. In the last analysis, nothing helps more than an association with parents and other adults whose good example the adolescent will wish to imitate and whose good opinion he or she cherishes.

Despite the occasional discovery of immoral practices among adolescents, it is well to keep in mind that these receive publicity while the fact that most adolescents behave normally goes without mention. They dream, they idealize, they masturbate more or less. They pass through periods of emotional upheaval and pain over their sexual urges, but most of them emerge from adolescence with much the same attitudes and strength of character and perhaps fewer scars than the preceding generation. A small number fail to work out of their childhood sexuality and remain homosexually latent or active.

The undue excitement some people display when homosexual behavior is discovered in some boy or girl often reveals their own inner tensions as much as it does a concern over the young person's problem. At such a time it is difficult to remember that it would be a most dull and uninteresting world if all men were completely masculine and all women completely feminine. Plainly this is not the case. The fact of the matter is that all of us are mixtures in various proportions of masculinity and femininity. Few great people fail to have some strong element of the opposite sex in their temperaments: perhaps the inner conflicts which develop out of their mixture of masculinity and femininity add fuel to their creative fires and aid in their production of even greater works of art, science, or philosophy. At any rate it is not surprising, though it is disconcerting and not at all something to be ignored, that in the course of their development adolescents sometimes drift into transitory homosexual episodes. The important matter is that these be understood for what they are. The passing experiences of adolescence demand handling different from that of true homosexuality.

That some great artists have been spurred on by such a conflict might be taken as evidence that we should hesitate to interfere in the masculine-feminine struggle. But history seems to show the contrary. Our significant and enduring cultural products for the most part have come from virile men and maternal women. For a man to possess little or no more femininity than is present in all of us is one thing; for him to retain a high degree of it is quite another. The idea that a high degree of unresolved femininity in a boy or masculinity in a girl is desirable ignores the mores of our society and the fundamental attitudes which derive from the need to perpetuate the race. The homosexual man or woman, or those with a high degree of identity with their own sex, do not, as a rule, marry and have children. There is a place in every society for these solitary, physically unproductive people, but all mankind's history goes counter to the idea that theirs is a state to be encouraged.

Parents, teachers, club leaders, and others of their own sex can attenuate excessive femininity in a boy or masculinity in a girl by their power to inspire imitation of themselves. Hero worship is a healthy concomitant of adolescence. Boys and girls wish to emulate an older person of their own sex, and they find it easier during this age period to copy and admire someone outside their families. This sort of association, and the satisfaction from an interest in things belonging to their own sex, often tips the balance. Without such an experience and rejected by their contemporaries of their own sex, they may tend to drift more and more away from the usual attributes of their own masculinity or femininity.

Real homosexuality is not common in boys or girls. The true homosexual is a very immature person who is very sick emotionally and who should have expert attention. However, it is of the utmost importance that true homosexual behavior not be confused with the sort of sexual experimentation which is common among adolescents, or with the excessive femininity in boys and masculinity in girls which we have just discussed. When given appropriate stimuli these young people sooner or later discard such attributes and renew their emotional growth toward maturity.

It is essential, too, that the effeminate sort of boy not be confused with the homosexual, or shunned or discussed as if he were one. Since all of us vary in the degree to which we are masculine or feminine, some men having feminine characteristics and some women having masculine ones, we should remember that these are not indices of homosexuality. The rather pretty, not very athletic, unaggressive boy should no more—on the basis of such traits—be labeled a homosexual than the football player. The tragedy of it is that the effeminate boy, lacking the strength and skill that would give him companions and recognition as an athlete, may be rejected by many, 'labeled,' and forced to fill his needs for companionship by associating with those who have no other friends — perhaps the true homosexuals. Any friend is to him better than no friend.

No matter how well they understand it, parents find even single episodes of homosexual behavior very disconcerting. There is always the fear that this is not a transient thing. A person with more training and experience than the average parent, and one less emotionally attached to the boy or girl, is better fitted to judge and to handle such a problem. Usually a frank discussion of the situation — an opportunity to correct any sex misinformation and to explain the childish and infantile nature of this practice — is a good beginning. An adolescent commonly responds well to this and to the suggestion that he or she has no wish to remain childish, and that a persistence in such activity might develop into a habit which will prevent really growing up to become a mature adult. Whoever does this will do well to continue the relationship with the boy or girl to the point of discussing both interests appropriate to their sex and the general matter of heterosexual relationships.

The boy or girl who comes from a home in which the parents themselves are emotionally immature, self-centered, and incapable of experiencing truly paternal and maternal love and care of their children may have great uncertainty about which parent to copy. Having lacked the warm love which is as important in infancy as food, they tend to turn their own capacity for loving to disturbing behavior in adolescence, for it is the time when they emerge from the emotional poverty of their childhood and begin to respond to the physical urges of sexuality. Having loved only themselves during the most crucial years of their development, they are now capable of loving only those like themselves and of their own sex. This is true homosexuality and it is plain that such a person, despite an outward veneer of adult behavior, is unable to establish the normal ties of love and affection so important for emotional health.

There are not, fortunately, many parents of the kind described above; and many children who do have such parents are kept from homosexuality by favorable and compensating factors. Consequently there is not a high incidence of true homosexuality in our society, but modifications and gradations of homosexuality occur frequently enough to make the problem one of considerable significance. Factors which promote it or discourage it need to be kept in mind. A boarding school or college can encourage latent homosexuality. Here at an impressionable age and in a vacillating period of life, teachers, coaches, and others are in a strong position to influence boys' and girls' emotional growth. The matrix for trouble will have been laid down long before they reach secondary school level, but there the adolescent with homosexual tendencies may be attracted to the latently homosexual teacher or fellow student. These teachers, some harsh, some kindly and mother-like, attract boys and girls who have personalities like their own. Drawn to imitate the feminine side of their families, boys find acceptance in such teachers, and justification for their impulses. Rarely such associations will lead to seduction by one or the other. More commonly, these teachers are sympathetic and kindly and provide associations which are extremely helpful to many students in this period when they are not yet ready to desert all that is feminine for the masculine competitive world. When these adults' latent homosexuality does not get beyond acceptable bounds and avoids the sort of overt behavior which is socially unacceptable, they are among the most valuable members of a teaching staff. A rigid attitude toward the *latently* homosexual teacher shows an utter lack of enlightenment and understanding and is unfortunate for both students and the institution.

One situation must be treated with the utmost care when it

arises in connection with a teacher, camp counselor, or club worker. We refer to accusations of perversion made by a boy or girl. The fact of the matter is that the majority of practicing homosexuals have, through long experience, found that it is of primary importance to restrict their practices to fields far from home. Scandal and discovery can so easily occur in school or club or camp that the majority are most careful to avoid any such activity with people who come in contact with them during their daily work. In fairness to these adults, it must be remembered that in adolescence the imagination is at its liveliest and daydreaming at its peak. An adolescent's imagination may well convert unconscious phantasies of his own into a real association with some adult to whom he is attracted, and, like children who believe their own imaginings, work himself into a firm conviction of the reality of something that exists only in his own dream life. For this reason, their evidence, though sometimes founded in fact, must be weighed with great caution and this possibility kept in mind.

Such then are the emotional problems with which sexuality faces the adolescent. Most of them work these problems out quite satisfactorily, some need a little help, and a few require expert assistance. Any one of them is very materially aided in this period of adjustment when he or she has a strong and healthy relationship with the parent of the same sex. With this sort of support most boys and girls move through this period of their lives with few scars and little anxiety.

IV

Achieving Independence:
Rebellion and Dependence

'I just can't manage Bill; he pays no attention to me; he's positively defiant. Sometimes he just doesn't answer and sulks; at other times he slams the door and goes out. But no matter what, he plain ignores me and does as he pleases. You'd think at sixteen he'd at least have better manners. I don't know what's gotten into him; he didn't used to be this way.'

Rebellion becomes a problem when the natural development of a young person's independence meets with consistent opposition. Adults want young people to grow up and to be-

45

come independent, but do not always seem willing to let them try. They forget that by continuing to help them they rob them of opportunities to learn to do for themselves. And when young people rebel, their defiance baffles and infuriates. Yet rebellion, though admittedly more difficult to live with, is really more praiseworthy and less frightening than is behavior which reflects a desire to remain dependent. All who work with and want to help young people need to understand rebellion: both adolescents and their parents may need help. It is often not an easy time for either.

The adolescent's imperative need to achieve independence, the gradual evolution of his behavior from the utter dependence of infancy toward the complete independence of adulthood, and the reasons for rebellion require as much understanding as do those essentials, love and security, which have for so many years been the basis of countless articles on the rearing of little children. That repetition is deserved: today too many people are handicapped by anxieties fostered by unhappy, insecure early years. However, the fact that young people should have increasing opportunities to become independent needs just as much emphasis. These opportunities they now need as they formerly needed constant protection and support. It is natural and proper for them to rebel; their rebellion is a problem only when it has to fight its way against parental domination and oversolicitude. To continue to protect adolescents, to continually thwart their attempts to develop independence, is to rob them of the abilities, confidence, and resiliency they must have in the demanding and unpredictable adult world they face. Later, secure and really independent, they will — we hope — be strong enough to realize how dependent we all are upon one another, how closely intertwined are our own safety and happiness with everyone else's. Continually to help them is constantly to remind them that we have no confidence in their ability to take care of themselves.

Bill caused his parents very little trouble or anxiety in his first fifteen years. Then during his second year of high school, things began to change, and a few months later his frantic mother sought help from his teachers and his scoutmaster. 'I can't figure Bill out; he ignores me; he acts as if he thinks I'm stupid, sometimes as if he hated me. I can't understand what's gotten into him. We do everything for him — we get him anything he wants. We try to help him with his school-work; we're careful what friends he makes; we don't let him wear himself out doing jobs after school. He used to tell me everything. Now, if I ask him where he's going, all he says is "Out," and if I try to find out whom he's been with, all he answers is "The gang." I tried for months to get him to have his teeth attended to before I finally gave up. Just last week we got a bill from the dentist: Bill had gone to him by himself and had never said a word to us. He's going around with some girl; I guess she's all right, but he won't bring her home. He won't talk about going to college. . . . Funny thing, though, every once in a while my husband and I get the feeling that he wants to talk — he sort of starts to and then seems to change his mind.'

That's adolescent rebellion, but to name it doesn't con-tribute much to understanding it. Obviously not all rudeness or defiance stems from a blocking of efforts to become inde-pendent, and any person frightened and driven to distraction from any cause is apt to revert to frantic behavior; but when there is evidence that an adolescent's attempt to grow up is being consistently thwarted, rebellion is a normal and desir-able, though unpleasant, phenomenon. Bill's behavior, if he were your Bill, would be hard to regard as desirable, but an adolescent's continued acceptance of overprotection can even-tually cause even more unhappiness.

Living with an organism while it is in the process of achiev-ing its independence is not always a happy experience. Bill started out totally dependent, literally tied to his mother. When he first tried to walk, it was with his hand in hers; slowly he broke away until he could walk by himself. This first evidence of his being able to do for himself made his parents very happy. They would have been very upset if he had not walked as early as Aunt Gertrude's boy, and they welcomed and applauded his early steps even though they were very awkward and even though he frequently fell. As he grew he gradually strove for more and more independence. Much later, now an adolescent with the size and strength to do a man's work, he wanted to be treated like one; he wanted to do his own schoolwork, choose his own friends, earn his own spending money, develop his own interests, have his own ideas. But his parents feared to have him try. They doubted his ability, his responsibility, and his judgment; and they believed it better for him to rely on theirs than to trust and develop his own. They feared he would make mistakes, would stumble; they feared he would make the same mistakes they had once made; and they dreaded the thought of his growing up and the thought of the time when he would need them no more. They forgot that his own awkward efforts would do him more good in the long run than the perfect things he could do with their help. They forgot that a transition from dependence to independence is normal, natural and something very much to be fostered. So they thwarted him — and he rebelled.

Rebellion is neither to be tossed off as 'just adolescence,' to be laughed at, to be infuriated by, or to be cried over. Certainly it is not to be met with stiff resistance. It needs to be understood as unpleasant evidence that a natural desire to grow up, to become a self-sustaining individual in one's own right, is being sought, albeit in a very awkward fashion. It is important to understand what is behind it, what it is heading toward, and why you feel about it as you do. Parents have an essential role in the production of these young people. We understand that, and we realize that children need our love and protection, that they be made to feel that they are wanted and that they be made to feel secure against inevitable threats. But as these young people change and grow up, *adults' roles, too, must change.* They must relax their protection and give young people ever-increasing opportunities to do for themselves. Their real job is to produce an adult, not a child. Children begin this life utterly dependent and utterly selfish: as they grow they must leave these unenviable states and attempt to reach the opposite poles.

Parents must occasionally assess the part their emotions play in their attitudes toward their children and attempt to discover what is behind their wishes and their plans for them. Is it their own shortcomings and failures that must be erased by their children's achievements? Are these successes ones the young people desire or have the aptitudes for, or are they only their parents' unfulfilled dreams? Is it parents' fears which force them always to think only of the dangers which threaten their growing son or daughter? Are their restrictions and restraints deeply colored by their own anxiety and insecurity? Is it their own emotional need for their children or for prestige that makes parents fear to let them grow up, leave, and strike out alone? Is this the basis for their secretly wishing that their child not grow up? Is it their children's faults, or just the shadows of the parents' own faults which they think they see in them, which make parents worry for the future? At this time when parents are being alternately renounced and sought by them — when their children too awkwardly strive for independence and next fear to accept it — it is hardly strange that parents alternately wish them to grow up and try to push them into maturity and then, fearing they are not ready to accept responsibility, refuse to let them try. By understanding this — how the parent feels and why, and what the boy or girl needs — the teacher, minister, or leader can do much to help hold the family together and to foster the boy's or girl's maturity.

Not only parents but also teacher, coach and scoutmaster need to watch that they do not retard the young person's maturity. 'He would do better in college if he had another year.' Perhaps it would be *easier*, but might it not be *better* for him to test his strength? Or he may want to give up crew. Well, after all, isn't his new interest in geology more maturing than the crew, worth more than his 'letter'? Is it that you need him at stroke? So when his interest wanes and he begins to deprecate his activity, give him freedom — or give him responsibility.

The female is indeed the gentler, less aggressive sex, but girls also need to develop their individuality and to gain independence. Thwarted in her efforts to grow up, a spirited girl becomes rebellious and can upset a home as completely as can her brother. When Mary was fifteen, a year after her father died, she and her mother were at swords' points. Dresses her mother bought her hung untouched in her closet; when questioned she would offer a limp excuse for not wearing them. She refused to help with the housework when her mother asked her to, but occasionally when her mother would go off for a holiday, she would return to find that Mary had cleaned the house from top to bottom. The neighbors couldn't believe that Mary refused her mother's request for help, that she was disobedient and impertinent, and that she never talked to her mother about her friends and her activities. She chattered endlessly to some of these neighbors and frequently helped them with their household chores. The telephone and Mary's going off on dates without permission caused the most violent scenes. Sometimes, when a boy would telephone Mary, her mother would fly into a rage and snatch the receiver from her.

Mary became more and more surly and evasive and stayed away from home more and more frequently until finally her mother sought out the high school principal. 'I do everything for her, I buy her clothes, I try to teach her how to do things properly, but she resents every suggestion I make. I try to protect her and she flies into a rage, screaming that she is no longer a baby. The only time she is fit to live with is when she has her own way.' The principal listened patiently, said he was sure he could help, and asked if the mother would talk to the school guidance counselor. At first she couldn't see that *she* needed help, she thought it was Mary who should be talked to, but she was desperate and agreed.

After first letting Mary's mother tell her story again, the guidance counselor suggested less rather than more restriction, and more rather than less freedom. He explained that, after all, the mother's tactics had failed and that an opposite approach could hardly be worse. It wasn't worse, of course; on the contrary it succeeded. Mary hadn't needed all that protection, all those suggestions. She had grown up more than her mother, still deeply feeling the loss of her husband, could bear to believe. And Mary, needing and wanting her own independence, failed to understand the deep emotion which made her mother try to hold her so close.

Understood as a manifestation of thwarted attempts at independence, adolescent rebellion is easier for a parent to tolerate. So, too, is it easier for them to sit by and see mistakes being made when they realize that mistakes made now mean fewer in the future. Young people's errors in choice of friends, their poor planning, their low grades in subjects parents could have helped them with, are hard to take, much harder than were the falls that accompanied those first halting steps; but parents need to realize that even as children learned to walk smoothly by letting them try, so will they become mature and able to protect themselves only by letting them do for themselves. It helps parents to understand this, and to loosen the reins, if some other adult — teacher, minister, doctor, no matter who it is whom they respect — explains and listens and takes some of the responsibility for the new way of meeting the situation.

So much for how adults feel. How about young people themselves?

It does not always require much restraint to produce signs

of rebellion. These young people are less confident than they care to admit; their show of defiance is balanced precariously. Angrily protesting that they are no longer babies, they fear independence, shrink from it, and may tomorrow seek the very help they reject today. The more confused and anxious, the less confident they are, the more defiantly rebellious they behave. Lacking in confidence, they bolster it with the noise, if not the substance, of power. The not answering, the slammed doors, the not talking, the shouting are rude — but they are much more than rudeness. They are ways of saying, 'I want to be independent, I want to handle this myself — whenever you come into it, it's just that much less my own.' As Bill groped toward independence, he seemed ruthlessly to reject his parents and to deny the value of all his parents' ideas and plans. He appeared to want to abandon those people to whom he had been so closely tied in his early years. It was as if, in order to help himself to break those close ties, he felt compelled to voice his low opinion of his parents and their ideas. Finding this break very difficult, to deny vociferously the worth of all he had loved and accepted made it easier for him.

Ironically, those adolescents who find the leaving of their parents and the acquisition of independence most difficult treat their parents the most cruelly: the more breaking away disturbs a boy or girl, the more fierce and childish will be the outbursts. The boy who swears at his mother, refuses to study, spits at his sister, slams doors, acts sullen, and comes to the table late, unwashed, and uncombed is not just rude and nasty and impossible. He is confused; he wants independence, yet fears it; and when he finally strives for it, he is thwarted. So, too, the girl who 'won't listen,' who insists on behaving the way she says other girls do, who won't help around the house, stays out late, mimics much older girls in dress and habits, and considers her parents old-fashioned. Confused and frustrated, they become at times frantic, and then like all frantic people they revert to unreasoning, impetuous, violent, and childish behavior.

Mary's and Bill's rebellion against their parents' well-meaning interference and overprotection was mild. But some of us value independence more highly than do others; and when an aggressive, strong-willed, independent personality in the making is frustrated, there is no peace in the house. Sam's rebellion was violent — but its cause was the same; it differed only in degree. At last his father sought out their minister. 'Sam won't talk to me — most of the time, that is. His language to his mother is awful — I wouldn't repeat the things he says — even to a simple innocent question like 'Did you change your socks?' Last night he didn't come home at all. We called up his school — he hadn't been there all week. His marks are terrible. I helped him with his chemistry one night and later I found he hadn't turned in his paper. One time he had me spend two hours helping him on the wrong lesson. Why would he deliberately do that? If his mother looks over his math and corrects something, he'll change it back to his own answer before he hands it in, even though he knows his answer was wrong. He never shows up at meals on time — we're tired of telling him to wash. We've tried everything. We've always done everything for him, maybe we've spoiled him. We help him; we discipline him — he's too big to beat but we punish him in every way we can think of. Nothing seems to do any good. We're licked. My wife is all upset — it just can't go on. He's bright, though, and he can be polite. He has lots of friends and he's very good to little children, and I know he would sit up all night with a sick dog. I don't really think he's a bad boy.'

Sam really wasn't bad! But he was a very upset young man who was certainly behaving very badly. At sixteen he was big enough and old enough to do things for himself, but he had never been allowed to. He deeply resented his parents' con-

tinual efforts to help him — their continual prodding and pry-
ing interference. Given a chance, he talked freely to his minister. 'It's always, "Where are you going? Study your French.
Don't go with that Tony — he's no good. Don't do it and never
mind why. Why don't you take Susie to the dance — that
Sally isn't your type. Wash your hands. Change your shirt.
Let me see your math." I used to try to talk about things, like
what went on at football or at a dance, but Mom couldn't wait
for me to finish before she'd ask how I did in history that day
— so I just don't talk any more. She goes through my bureau
— I don't know what she's looking for. If I do my math, she
tries to check it and correct it. I'm tired of telling her that it's
supposed to be what *I* can do.'

He had many other things on his mind — it was easy to see
why he rebelled and why he behaved so badly. Patiently Sam's
minister explained these things to his parents: that he did not
need punishment and did not need to have the rebellion
knocked out of him; what he really needed was to become
more independent. He was not as tough as he seemed; when
his minister suggested several things that he do all by himself,
he was obviously hesitant to try, but he reluctantly agreed,
and, not forced, not given too much too soon, he gradually
developed more confidence. His parents' overprotection and
oversolicitude had not only made him the rebellious boy they
saw, but it had done something much worse — it had arrested
the development of his confidence. Driven away from his
parents by their annoying suggestions and questions about
trivial matters, he did not feel he wanted to talk to them about
the important things that were bothering him. Given normal
opportunities to do for himself, he would have long since
been much more grown up.

The seeds of serious rebellion are sown in the early years
and in the home. When there is conflict between the parents; when there is nagging and sarcasm and little effort to
work out problems rationally and unemotionally; when chil-

dren are not trusted and not given every opportunity to do and to think for themselves; when parents, unhappy with their own lives, try to relive them in their children, there is a good chance that in early adolescence a normal desire to become independent will appear as gross defiance, not just rudeness. Prevention starts with a home and school in which children never doubt that they are wanted, where there are good will and companionship, where parents and teachers teach respect, loyalty, and cooperation not by a show of power but by their own good example; a home and school where problems are discussed in the open and worked out cooperatively; a home where each other person's own needs and interests and personality, not one's own, are the basis for help and suggestions; a home and school where ideas are shared and opinions, though immature, have a hearing, where there is no more hesitation to withhold praise than to offer censure, where mistakes are tolerated, even expected, and not laughed at.

Edith's only slightly uneven hem and Joe's not quite perfect mortise mean more to their development than the precision job mother or father could have turned out for them. They want, and need, to do for themselves; their early efforts deserve encouragement, not carping criticism or reluctant praise or the impatient 'We can't wait all day — give it to me.'

The way their friends do things and consequently the way they want to do them is worth consideration even though it may not be an adult's way. Adolescents are no longer completely dependent on their families for emotional support, for advice, for companionship; they have their own crowd or gang. That they can be happy away from home, that they have become to a great extent independent of it, should be a source of satisfaction. Just because all that Edith and Joe now seem to want from home are clothes, food, shelter, money, and of course the car, does not mean that they do not still have strong emotional ties to their home and parents. They have transferred their companionship needs to their own age group. They have not lost all respect for parents, teachers, and other adults, but now their group's ideas are, to a great extent, theirs. They are not ungrateful or without affection — they are only loosening, not severing, their ties. They are learning to live with their contemporaries, learning to take their criticism, noticing their ways, hoping for their praise. They will leave that phase too, we hope. They'll lose their dependence on their gang and go on to take their places in the world and to make homes of their own — their next step toward adulthood. Unfortunately a few, from fear and overprotection and dominance, will never become really adult. Edith needs to lose her dependence on her 'crowd' and Joe his on his 'gang' just as their parents need to be left for a more mature, more responsible, more independent, more adult way of living.

Nothing is of more importance to an adolescent's development than the manner in which inevitable conflicts are settled. Veto power, emotionalism, selfishness, traditionalism have no more right in the home or school or club than they do in the United Nations. 'I haven't time to explain, do as I say' should be reserved for such times as when the house is on fire. 'Get in at ten tonight, and I don't want any discussion about it' may get you back to your newspaper sooner, but it is hardly as good an object lesson in diplomacy as 'Say, Joe, what's the real scoop on this midnight stuff?' A willingness to listen to the other side, to put yourself in his place, teaches by example the sort of interpersonal relationships which would make this world a better place for all of us. But not to be in control, to refuse to guide the family or school or club, to leave young people entirely on their own whims and interests, breeds insecurity and anxiety. Until they're ready to ship out alone, they need to feel that the helm is in strong, capable hands.

So much for early prevention, so much for understanding what rebellion is. The extreme instances of rebellion are the unhappy incidents and events which follow when adults rely on authority to produce the sort of respect which can only grow out of good relationships; when adults continue to thwart every attempt at growing up; when through fearing that their children will be hurt, and failing to appreciate the importance of their attaining independence, or needing them themselves, parents refuse to let them go, and try and try again to squelch any signs of rebellion. Out of these come discord and runaways.

Rebellion really can be desirable. Suppose an adolescent were to remain a dependent child? What sort of future does that promise? Fortunate and happy the home or school or club where maturity and independence are approached gradually, but it is better to have bizarre hair-dos and slammed doors, unheeded warning and monosyllables, than no evidence of a desire to stand alone. It is obviously independence, not rebellion, which deserves encouragement and applause; but when adolescents' natural striving toward independence is thwarted, their rebellion is more praiseworthy than is submission. Savage rebellion, like war, is an unhappy business. But fear of responsibility, a preference for dependence, an apparent fear to enter into womanhood or manhood, a failure to struggle against too-tight reins — those are a more disheartening spectacle than is defiance. Few of us can view complacently the prospect of the spiritless boy or girl accepting today oversolicitude and domination who thereby gives promise of tomorrow relinquishing their remaining hope of independence to the blandishments of a dictator.

Where there is dependence, the scene in school or home is more quiet, but the future is more forbidding. Phil's mother couldn't understand that. And later she couldn't understand his failure in his senior year in high school. She, as she put it, 'had done everything for him.' That, of course, was exactly it. Not being allowed to do for himself, it was inevitable that either he remain totally dependent or that he become resentful. Phil's marks were terrible. He was fed up with school, but he had no thought of doing anything but dragging along. During his grade school years he had done very well, and there was no reason to doubt his ability. He talked freely about his mother, of her boundless energy and the efficient way she handled things both at home and in his father's business. Phil had always been told exactly what to do, exactly what to wear, exactly where to go. He had never tried to make plans for himself; his mother always planned things so very well. She bought his clothes, planned his summers, told him what girl to take out, what college to try for. But it was not her dominance and overprotection which was most disturbing: it was Phil's failure to rebel. Dependent and irresponsible by nature, neither independence nor responsibility had been fostered by others and now was not being sought by the boy himself. His school thought him 'such a nice boy — perhaps a little lazy, but he'll grow out of it. He's no real trouble at all — not like some of our boys.' He played football, but never hard enough to make the team; smaller, less able boys beat him out. 'Too eager,' he called them. He wrote well, but he'd never take the pains to polish his themes — 'If you do well, then they always expect you to.' He was an expert swimmer but he wouldn't take a waterfront job — 'I'd rather let somebody else worry.' Never leading, always hanging back; sensitive and not seeking the knowledge and prestige which would bring him responsibility — there he was, a beautiful machine, wrapped in cellophane.

Conformity and docility, which make for 'low nuisance value' in the classroom and home, strike fear in the hearts of those who want democracy and our sort of culture to survive. The orderliness and discipline of the ant world must often have seemed heaven to a harassed parent or weary teacher, but its excessive conformity seems to have stifled the progress that the free play of individuality permits. Neither wanton individuality nor selfish aggression is commendable in the individual or the state; but its counterpart, because its undermining influence is so quiet, too seldom worries us. Few of us think the status quo perfect, but many of us resent and thwart and fear those independent individuals who would try to change the shape of things for the better. We punish and we fear aggressors, but we are endangered as much by those who so readily yield, who never venture, and who shirk all responsibility.

Rebelliousness needs to be properly channeled, not condemned: independence and the fruits of individuality need to be cherished. It is no less imperative that the extremes of conformity and dependence be given attention and that when found they be startled out of 'their obsequious salute to power and to the status quo.' Judge Learned Hand has warned us eloquently: 'Our dangers, as it seems to me, are not from the outrageous but from the conforming; not from those who rarely and under the lurid glare of obloquy upset our moral complaisance, or shock us with unaccustomed conduct, but from those, the mass of us, who take their virtues and tastes, like their shirts and their furniture, from the limited patterns which the market offers . . . all confidently assured that nothing was lacking to their complete realization of the Human Ideal. Over that chorus the small voice of the individual sounds not even the thinnest obligato; it seems senseless and preposterous to sing at all . . . Our problem, as I see it, is how to give the mannikin, assailed on all hands with what we now so like to call propaganda, the chance of survival as a person at all, not merely as a leaf driven by the wind, a symbol in a formula.'

Not all the frustration which sharpens up the signs of rebellion is provided by mothers or the alma mater who refuse to let their offspring grow up. Fathers who plan too much, who are too ambitious for their sons, who want them to succeed where they have failed, can unwittingly do just as much harm. Ted had done very well in his first two years at high school. He was big and mature, and in his third year at school his family expected great things of him. That fall, however, his marks were atrocious. His father blamed his failures on football and insisted that the boy give up athletics. But Ted did no better in school; as a matter of fact he did worse, and with each poor report from school his father piled on more restrictions. Football over, his father had nothing to blame but 'laziness' and 'a lack of appreciation of all that had been done for him.' Finally, his patience exhausted, and everything save studying, eating, and sleeping prohibited, he said he was through with the whole business and that Ted's mother could now do as she wished about it.

Ted talked very little and seemed surprised that anybody could be interested in *his* opinions. Later he got the idea that it was, after all, his problem, that it was what *he* thought, what *he* had to say, that was important. Before long he blurted out that after all, he didn't suppose his opinion mattered — his father always settled everything and that try as he would, he guessed he was trapped and eventually would have to do just what his father said. What he wanted more than anything else was the chance to have some opinions of his own and a chance to try them out, a chance to try to live his own life. All his life decisions had been made for him. He had always been told what was best for him. He had never been asked what he thought, what he wanted. His school, his courses, his vacations had all been good — in fact excellent — choices, but he had had no part choosing them and it seemed to him that it was always going to be that way. He had made many attempts to act or to appear grown up, but they had always been thwarted. When he wanted a door key, he was told there was no need for him to have one unless he planned to stay out too late at night. When he asked for an allowance, he was told that he didn't need one; that he could have money when he wanted it. When he asked if he could get a job, he was told that the family had plenty of money and that there was no reason for him to work; when he announced that he would like to be an architect, he was told it was a silly idea and that he should plan to study law. Ted had taken the only way he knew to defeat his father. But now, with his counselor's help, both he and his parents approached the situation in a more constructive fashion. It took some doing to get him to see that he was really defeating himself, and that there was a better way to win out.

Few parents are so possessive, protective, and lacking in appreciation of a boy's individuality and his need to become independent as were Bill's or Ted's or Sam's. But too often we fail to understand how essential it is that an adolescent become self-reliant, that he have his own ideas and plans and responsibilities, and that he develop his own personality. The career a boy chooses can be of less significance than that he have ideas about it, that it be his own choice. He can, and should, be guided; but a poor choice of his own is better than for him to have no ideas and, like Phil, only blindly to follow someone else. His own latch key, his own bank account, a job, buying and caring for his own clothes and possessions, sharing in the family's problems, doing for others — all these develop a sense of responsibility and independence and make him feel that he is trusted and thought of as a person trying to become an adult. There is everything to gain, and nothing to lose, by efforts to help him grow up. A boy may occasionally come in late by the door instead of through the window, or he may buy a shirt or a tie you wouldn't wear on a dark night — but he won't do these too often. It may be painful to watch him try to become mature, but it isn't half as disheartening as to find that he doesn't want to do so.

It is no less important that girls develop their personalities, their own individuality and independence. This does not mean that they should become like men; indeed, it is quite the opposite. The more they develop their natural traits, the more confident and less fearful they become, the less dependent they are and the less they will hesitate to become feminine and to assume all the responsibilities that womanhood entails. Demure, dependent little girls are not truly feminine; they fear the demands of adult life and hide timidly in their mothers' shadows, confounding fearfulness with femininity. They are just as much to be pitied as their seemingly courageous sisters who escape into masculine pursuits to avoid those accompaniments of womanhood which they secretly fear. We need to help the adolescent girl, during her period of vacillating between wanting and fearing womanhood, to be more feminine, to be free of fears, to be strong and independent enough to be her true self.

Adolescents thrive on responsibility — the more you give them, the better they learn to handle it. It is only when they are given too much too soon, when without any preparation too much is expected of them, or when responsibility is too long withheld and then thrown at them all at once that they come a cropper. This rebellion is a straining at the bit; it is solved by loosening, not by tightening, the reins.

If young people are to develop into mature, independent, self-reliant men and women capable of respect for authority and for the rights and needs of others, they must be given ever-increasing opportunities to venture. They need to put meaning into those personalities which love and security gave so fine an early start. That beginning was ideal, but it was only a preparation for living. In adolescence they need to practice living like the adults they are beginning to be. As they grow they must learn to protect themselves, to develop their own attitudes and interests, their own personalities. When they have done this, they will be ready for *interdependent*, not independent living — truly mature living in a peaceful world. If we continue to run their lives, continue to protect them, we can only leave them without protection, without confidence in themselves and without minds of their own.

V

The Severe Disorders

As we look back over the various troubles that beset adolescents, we see that they run the gamut all the way from homesickness to schizophrenia to brain tumor. How shall such ills be distinguished, their severity evaluated, and proper treatment for each begun? Can anyone who has not had the careful training of the neurologist or psychiatrist expect to recognize these disorders? These are important questions: on occasion life may be sacrificed because a serious disturbance seemed to the inexperienced adult to be mild.

Not even the most skilled and experienced medically trained clinician can discover every potentially malignant illness in its beginnings; however, he is far more likely to suspect a serious condition than any other professional person. But mothers and teachers are in the best position to discern the first slight changes in manner and behavior that warrant more careful scrutiny: they are usually the first to notice that something is wrong. Their observations — though their fears may not always prove to be warranted — are of great value, for many of the disturbances of adolescence are slow to develop and are most efficiently treated in their early stages. Their prompt recognition is not merely a means of quickly restoring emotional health but may be a means of averting tragedy.

Treatment of many of these ills spans a wide range. Now and then striking changes occur in the behavior of a disturbed adolescent in response to no more than a slight change in a parent's way of handling him or her. On the other hand, psychotherapy of two or three years' duration has been necessary to release a severely upset youngster from his inner conflicts. In general, however, the adolescent's problems have shallow roots, and because of their flexibility and resilience they usually respond with gratifying ease and speed to proper treatment.

It should always be borne in mind that treatment of real emotional disorders requires skill and experience. Any apparently serious problem should be referred to a trained person; even in the case of a minor ailment if a teacher, coach, camp counselor, or guidance worker finds after a talk or two that little or no improvement has occurred in an adolescent's complaints, a physician should be consulted. It is these people's function to see that these young people get the help they need. It is obviously not always they themselves, however, who are best fitted to give it.

What labels should be used to name the emotional ills of adolescence? In our opinion the fewer employed the better both for the patient and for the advancement of our knowledge about these matters. At present we suffer from a plethora of labeling: it is as though we become uneasy if something cannot have a name or a number. Yet we know that it is a characteristic of the immature personality to wish things to be clearly defined: to such a one, everything must be good or bad, right or wrong. It is only with emotional maturity that we begin to see all the gradations in the world around us and can accept the disquieting variations between the extremes. Therefore, rather than to attempt with infinite care to name most of the ills of adolescence, we believe it best for lay and professional helper alike to focus thought and attention on the troubled boy or girl. It is Ben or Alice, each with a unique background and quality of character, who is of importance, not the name of his or her ailment or the ailment itself. If after considerable thought you label Ben 'an interesting case of psychomotor epilepsy' or Alice 'a typical case of psychogenic dysmenorrhea,' you may have become intrigued by an illness and lost some of your interest in the person. You may then treat and think about them as you would a fixed problem, not as people whose problem only resembles those which others have experienced.

Admittedly, for purposes of study and orderly discussion, we sometimes need to use names and labels. Our point is that all this is secondary, that the matter of primary importance is the individual. The adolescent is very important to himself, and he must be very important to you if you are to do your best for him. More than at any other time of life adolescence is an age when the importance of each individual is paramount. They are struggling mightily for recognition from their companions and from adults around them. How often we hear them say, 'If they'd only take me seriously!' In truth this is the need of every man and woman under the sun.

It is not our purpose in the next few pages to encourage parents or teachers to become diagnosticians or psychotherapists. Our intent is to give more people a better understanding of the causative factors of some of the more severe emotional diseases with the hope that a comprehension of the role which these factors play will make for a more widespread prevention of the less serious ailments. A discussion of serious disease often serves to throw those causative factors which also initiate minor ailments into sharper focus. It is important to remember, of course, that every factor that is sometimes associated with a mental illness does not always mean that trouble is present or inevitable. Many adolescents survive broken homes, few boys who prefer to sit and read to playing football get into trouble, not many girls who give up boys for softball are headed for an emotional upset. These may be warning signals — but they are just that, not a diagnosis.

Few adolescents develop real psychoses, although many go through periods when their behavior may temporarily be difficult to distinguish from such a condition as schizophrenia, one of their most serious illnesses. Indeed, at the onset and height of much less severe disorders, when they are nothing more than temporarily confused, psychologists find adolescents giving responses to such tests as the Rorschach very like those which one obtains from schizophrenics. Unless the psychologist is both cautious and also experienced in the use of tests like the Rorschach, his interpretation of an adolescent's response will be pessimistic and in grave error.

It is important to remember that after a very short time a boy or girl who has seemed very ill may swing back to normal. Though they may be completely out of touch with reality, one cannot be sure until there has been an opportunity for several days' observation that what one sees is more than the response of an adolescent whose feelings have become extremely upset during a period of adjustment to one of the many stresses that upset them all. Adolescents frequently show symptoms which would be most ominous and diagnostic of severe and long mental illness in an adult, but which in them are only transient and, though demanding expert attention, not a justifiable cause of despair. They are resilient, they have great capacity for change, and they are in an unsettled period with wide swings in emotional reaction. Just as is true of their physical growth, so must their emotional status be cautiously evaluated and judged, whenever possible, over a period of time rather than as of the present moment.

The nature of the stresses which act as causative factors of emotional illness is not always clear, and often it is true to say of them, 'Things are seldom what they seem.' For instance, the sadness that comes with homesickness may develop into a state in which boys or girls withdraw all interest and attention from people and things about them: they may become so wrapped in thoughts of home that their school and their companions seem unreal to them. Constantly dreaming of home and thinking of themselves, they are unable to grasp their schoolwork except in fragments, and these, being disconnected, confuse and bewilder them. This confusion worries them and they ask themselves, 'What is going on in my mind?' 'Am I going crazy?' Fed by this anxiety, their confusion soon reaches that state where nothing is clear, and they sit, the picture of bewilderment, rubbing their foreheads as if to push the clouds away, making comments or asking questions which seem to us to make little sense. This, of course, isn't schizophrenia. It is homesickness; but the daydreaming, the confusion, the withdrawal from usual pursuits could lead one to an erroneous quick impression.

Anger, too, can be one of the bases of adolescent schizophrenic-like behavior. This is not the wholesome, outspoken anger of the quick-tempered, but the smoldering, deep anger that never reaches up into consciousness. Like molten lava this kind of anger waits for the time when its pressure will be strong enough to blow off the top. As the pressure grows, it seeks other outlets and may become so great that it breeds a wish to destroy not only those for whom one has close ties but also anyone who meets one's fancy. As a protection from this wish, all things, all people, are made to seem unreal.

Now unreality is usually a fixed sensation in schizophrenia. It is as if much of the personality has been turned backward in time and lives at an infantile level: thumb-sucking, playing with bowel movements, and absorption in infantile play and mannerisms are common. All things outside are warped and distorted; all sense of time and place are lost; people seem changed and familiar faces are unrecognized; memories of voices are heard again; primitive impulses checked since early childhood tell him to hide, to kill, to attack, to flee, or even to punish himself by taking his own life. Many boys and girls have similar experiences, but of course in a very limited and diluted form. Their resiliency is great, and with the emotional support of loving parents and their own friends, they ride through any such brief threats and enter adulthood with few if any scars. Again it is imperative to be slow to make a judgment or diagnosis or to predict the future outcome especially when the symptoms are of very recent onset or very few: one swallow does not make a summer.

Unfortunately, however, at times these warning signals not only demand attention but prove really to have indicated serious trouble. How is it that some adolescents do not fare so well and, failing to master these outbursts, suffer temporary breakdowns, or — rarely — develop a long and severe psychosis? For the answer we must first look at the experiences of infancy. The infant suddenly finds himself in a cold, bright, noisy world. A kindly soul's booming voice breaks the silence and starts his tears. As the infant grows he is subject to more and more assaults and challenges. In these years his primary need is still his mother, her love and attention and companion-ship. When these are lacking he becomes fearful and in his anxiety seeks the shelter and security he knew in infancy. Instead of confidently stepping out to meet the world, feeling the strength of those who support him, now fearful he turns backward, retreating within himself and toward the thought and activities of his earlier life.

These fears and uncertainties are unlikely to overpower an adolescent and produce such a reaction if he or she has the security and strength that a background of loving parents brings. Hurts and reverses don't have to be avoided — they can't be — but they will be met and overcome and the child's growth in wider activity and depth of activity will go on. New ties with an ever-widening circle of people around the child are made possible; first father, then brothers and sisters, then other relatives, then those other children and adults outside his own family whom he often sees. At the same time that the child is forming emotional ties to others, strong bonds are also being made between him and things. A woolen bunny, a floppy-eared bear take on personality and meaning. All through life, however, there is an intermittent struggle of varying intensity against deep and powerful wishes to return to the security of infancy. During adolescence these impulses gain new strength and produce unpredictable and often frightening patterns. It is then that the self-love of infancy revives and so we see reactions varying all the way from that of the normal boy and girl spending hours before the mirror in those self-worshipping rituals which serve as a temporary escape from the problems of their lives to the abnormal complete withdrawal which the schizophrenic seeks as a source of inner security and reassurance.

Granted good heredity, the implications for prevention are clear. Beyond this there is little to do but to be on the alert for early symptoms of schizophrenia and at the same time to avoid the errors which are inevitable if one forgets either the resiliency of youth or the extensive turmoil and reliving of their early life which is common to all normal adolescents.

Ambivalence — loving and hating — is one of the contradictory facets of human nature. It seems to go on in all of us at deep levels in our personalities with little or no surface evidence of its activity. Why do we at times dwell on all the dire misfortunes that might befall a loved one? One of us will fear for the safety of a relative or friend, while another equally close in his relationship will have the attitude 'Oh, he'll be all right.' Often such fears, openly expressed, seem to be a cloak for deeper-seated wishes of quite the opposite kind, but why some of us occasionally have conscious fears for the safety of someone we love and concurrent unconscious wishes that dire events befall them is not clearly understood. Such feelings are so against all we have been taught to think and believe that they are hard to accept.

So, too, can we alternately seem to love and hate ourselves. When we are truly depressed, it is as though all our hate for another was turned upon ourselves. Feeling this way, we consider ourselves worthless, bad, and unfit to hold up our heads among our fellows. When the feeling is strong enough this self-hatred may go so far as to suggest that killing ourselves is the only fit punishment.

The depressed or suicidal adolescent is one who has never developed beyond an emotionally infantile state, or is one who has regressed emotionally to such a level. When an adolescent does become depressed it is usually not difficult to distinguish between mild and serious states. These boys and girls do not speak freely; their sorrowful looks, the low tone and slowness of their speech, are in sharp contrast with their former selves. Since the depression arises out of childish thinking and feeling, much of what a boy or girl in such a state says will be unreal.

This very ridiculousness unfortunately leads adults into serious errors in judgment as to the seriousness of the adolescent's intentions. An adolescent's threat that he is going to take his life may often be a desperate attempt to gain attention, but it is nonetheless worthy of careful investigation. Even though the threat may be halfhearted, one cannot be sure; it is a chance a gambler would never take; and in any event the fact that he or she openly seeks attention so desperately in itself demands that something be done.

When there is any doubt about the seriousness of a boy's or girl's intention of suicide, it is helpful to get them to talk about the means they have considered for taking their life. This may seem at first a foolhardy thing to do, but its value becomes apparent when we remember that up until that time this young person had kept his thoughts to himself and had not put them into words. Just putting his or her thoughts into words turns the cold light of reality on them and diminishes their power.

The force of strong feelings of aggression are often underestimated because it is not pleasant even to admit their existence, let alone their extent. Faced with a multitude of poorly disguised examples of primitive rage and hatred in our present-day society, we shun this new unpleasantness. As civilized persons we feel we should attempt to control our primal passions, and we train our children with this end in mind. Inevitably they emerge from childhood with many of their primitive impulses repressed and bottled up within their unconsciousness.

But the repression of primitive urges and passions does not seem to eliminate them. In fact, when the automatic controls aren't strong enough, they may break loose, and then the results of these breaks fill the columns of the 'yellow journals.' Or these feelings, being repressed, still continue to exert their influence and appear in many forms. Psychosomatic disorders, for instance, have a repressed rage as an accompaniment: in one, his stiff arthritic joints may reflect this person's attempt to hold them rigid so that he will not kick or hit or even kill someone close to him who has unwittingly failed to satisfy his insatiable infantile needs.

Fortunately these feelings of suppressed hate need neither break loose nor be expressed as symptoms: an adolescent can learn to relieve them in many satisfactory ways. The device of understatement is one. We say we are 'putting it mildly' in order to intensify the feeling in what would otherwise seem to be a very bland comment. Overpoliteness serves a similar purpose. And so, without words, does the too-ready smile, which reminds the skeptic of the baring of fangs! In folklore the Trojan Horse story is reminiscent of the same idea: 'Timeo Danaos et dona ferentis.'

A teacher's harshness and severity, too, can really be a relief to many adolescents, though they may appear to resent them. They furnish an adversary for a young person's unexpressed feelings. A really kind teacher, though desirable for some, may cause uneasiness in other immature adolescents, particularly those who are trying to establish their own personalities. These need someone to struggle against, so that they may test and strengthen themselves.

Ed was that sort of fellow. He had never been sure of himself. 'Ever since I was a little fellow I guess I never knew what was coming off. When I'd go home after school, I'd likely find my mother drunk or drinking. Then my father would come home and be angry at everyone, or he'd just stay at his office and work.' Later when Ed did very poorly in school his parents said it was because his teachers were too harsh and didn't give him enough attention. But Ed, like many such boys, had a very different story. The only teacher he really liked was a frustrated, sarcastic chap who really deserved the vulgar nickname by which successive generations of boys had known him. 'He's a stinker, but you know where you stand with him. I make a crack at him once in a while and does he ever take my head off. But I don't ever dare go into his class unprepared. I'd rather have them all that way — not like Droopy — he's the mamma's boy type. He's easy on you but I don't trust him; I turn in a lousy paper or don't do any work and all he does is ask me if I feel well or if I understood the assignment. You can't seem to make him mad.' Confused, depressed, uncertain of what he wanted or where he was going, surrounded with acquaintances but without friends, rejected by his girl ('she's the only person I ever thought gave a hang about me,') he needed strong, aggressive teachers with whom he could trade punches.

Another valuable outlet for aggressive feeling is action, even though that action is not openly aggressive in nature. Difficult problems, hard work, challenges of all kinds are desirable. Challenges too, especially with boys, are of help in enabling them to struggle to assert the masculinity within them and to submerge those feminine impulses they find disturbing. Competitive sports furnish a good outlet for aggression in early adolescence, though it would seem wise for adults also to encourage other and increasingly mature outlets for these aggressive impulses as boys grow up.

A job is so frequently helpful to an apparently recalcitrant and hopeless boy that work itself is worth more attention than it gets in these days when education seems to many to be all important. Education is important and desirable, but many aggressive boys find little challenge in systems geared to the average and committed to educate all with little regard of their ability or behavior. Jerry's parents had thought that a private school would solve what they called *their* problem. Jerry had refused to study, was a ringleader of a gang that stole and destroyed property; he behaved in the obnoxious, immature fashion of the 'drugstore cowboy.' Three private schools gave up. He called their athletics 'kid stuff' and the studies 'a lot of useless tripe.' Reluctantly, Jerry's parents agreed to let him get a job. Even after all these failures they still thought it was their problem and that it was dreadful for him to leave school at sixteen. But given the problem as *his*, told to go ahead and get his own job and plan thereafter to support himself, Jerry changed as completely as one could ever expect. Now he had something he could put his teeth in, something legitimate to boast about to his former gang. He earned his own money, and he was more careful with it. Later he began to see that some education would be a help.

Other more mature outlets are to be found in the competitive nature of business, in fighting for causes, and in the entire gamut of reform. At different ages there are not only varying needs for but also a varying capacity to adapt to emotionally mature goals. What is suitable for one person and what will help another are not always the same. One adolescent should give up football in college and move into the world of books; another should be thankful that colleges — or clubs — continue to offer him sports as his major outlet. Only if what is best for the individual is kept in mind can we hope to reach higher levels of emotional maturity and lessen the world's store of neurotic and immature behavior.

Not all boys feel or behave in this fashion or have these needs. It is the youths who have a surplus of aggression or who become homesick, depressed, or suicidal who may need these outlets. There is no one way to treat all boys, let alone one way to handle the ones with such disorders. A fractious youngster who invariably rebels at harshness may need and be most co-operative with a kindly and gentle teacher. Only by knowing each of them and each one's needs can you hope to do what is best for them. Fortunately only a few really require special handling; most of them get along reasonably well with all kinds of people. It is when things threaten to go badly that some adjustment must be made. Free of excessive aggression, not prey to wide swings of love and hate, in short emotionally mature, the likelihood of depression and suicide is remote.

VI

Anxiety States

Although severe emotional disorders are uncommon during adolescence, it is a rare boy or girl who has passed through adolescence without having a period of anxiety which was at least temporarily upsetting. After all, during this transition period all adolescents must adjust their feelings about sex and their relationships to their parents; seek independence; build up their own personalities and confidence by means of those achievements which bring recognition; and meet the confusions which school, religion, adults' behavior, death, and a host of other matters may bring. That all of these often constitute problems does not mean that most adolescents do not solve them quite adequately. Most of them do, and the period during which confusion and worry are handicapping is usually quite brief. However, for one reason or another, some problems are more troublesome for some adolescents than for others, and they either cause, or act as the 'last straw' in, the development of an 'anxiety state.' This is no more than to say that for the time being this young person's problems are more than he can handle: they, to a certain extent, are running him, are keeping him from working and living as happily and efficiently as he should.

Anxiety takes many forms. It may occur at a deep, unconscious level and be evidenced only by some symptom typical of physical illness, or it may appear close to the surface of consciousness in the form of those body responses which we associate with fear. A dry mouth, rapid breathing, fast heart rate, dilated pupils, 'gooseflesh,' hair 'standing on end,' a tight or sinking feeling in the stomach, and taut muscles are all part of a fear reaction. They indicate readiness to fight whatever has suddenly threatened or to flee if the threat proves too great to overcome. Such a state of readiness cannot be maintained very long because our reserves of hormones and chemicals which produce it are small and quickly exhausted.

Man's mind has two parts: the conscious, where most external and internal activity goes on at a level which can be put into words; and the unconscious, where much that goes on is not put into words but where, because of the nature of its ties to the entire nervous system, its power to stir the body is great. An unknown sound, for example, may produce a different response in each of three listeners: a sound from a dark wood's path will suggest a wild beast to one, a dangerous serpent to another, and a stray cow to a third. The first listener will take to his heels; the second will freeze to the spot to avoid being struck; and the third will only call out, 'Ho, bossy!' Each one will have the bodily feelings of fear, though of considerably varying degree and duration.

Anxiety, like fear, has its origin in something unknown, something mysterious. Not being known, whatever it is which we experience cannot be put into words; we don't know the sound, the shape, the event for what it really is so we can't call it by name or describe it in words. In short, we do not understand it. For instance the adolescent, seeing his parents in conflict, may be mystified and anxious. It is upsetting to him, just as was that eerie sound, for the dependent little boy within him who *feels* and still regards Father and Mother as his strong bulwark against the threats of the outside world. But now things are strange; his strong defenses have been lost and all that is left is uncertainty. Faced with the possibility of their divorce, he may perhaps feel triumphant for now he will have Mother all to himself; but this will quickly be erased by the feelings of disloyalty to his father, who has meant so much to him. In short he doesn't know where he stands; he doesn't understand; it is something unknown and mysterious — so he is *anxious*.

These conflicting emotions create a storm of feeling deep within him that cannot be fully resolved until he has expressed them in words and come to understand them. If they remain unresolved, at an unconscious and wordless level, they will seek and find some other outlet. They may drain energy from his conscious activity so that he will not concentrate on his studies and he may daydream and be unable to recall what he dreams about; or his conflict may be shunted into his sympathetic nervous system and cause such symptoms as nausea, diarrhea, or headache. These are the things that are likely to happen if his feelings about this situation are not expressed, if he does not come to understand them.

Conflict between their parents and the attendant insecurity in their homes is but one of the many reasons for adolescents' anxiety. Poor progress in school, their sexual adjustment, unpopularity, and nowadays the prospect and uncertainty of military service, are frequently upsetting. Those whose childhood has permitted the development of independent and emotionally stable personalities take most of these matters in their stride. It is the dependent, insecure young people who are bowled over, and it is these we need to help to become more secure, more independent. Whatever can be done to foster those states will obviously be of real preventive value.

Jim had always leaned heavily on his mother for protection. She helped him with his homework, she kept him from school when he ate little or no breakfast or when he said his stomach was upset, she shielded him from his father's sporadic attempts to 'make a man of him.' Nothing was too good for Jim. He was sent to a private school 'because he needed individual attention.' At that point he did! He had been helped so much that he couldn't help himself and it took the extra effort of several teachers to get him into college. He had a superficial charm, good manners, good looks, and more than enough intelligence to permit him to do very well in his studies. In college, however, he did miserably.

'They don't seem to take any personal interest in him, doctor. You have to understand Jim. He's lost weight and he doesn't eat well. I think something's worrying him.' It was. He was eating little, he had lost weight, and he had all manner of gastrointestinal symptoms. At first he offered one rationalization after another as the cause of his failure, but it was evident that the main trouble was simply that he had started off doing little or no studying and soon was far behind and in the sort of fix that only a more purposeful and independent boy could hope to conquer. Jim wasn't that sort; he just gave up. And then it dawned on him that if he were to flunk out he would no longer be deferred from military service. And how would his mother feel; what would his father do; what would his friends think? Vacillating among these thoughts, he neither faced his fundamental problem nor worked out his present one; and from week to week his anxiety increased. His dilemma was more than he could stand. He became panicky, lost his appetite, and began to have 'stomach trouble.' 'Stomach trouble' had been his means of getting out of school when he was a little boy, and now he could rely on it to get him out of college before he was 'fired' — and it might exempt him from military service too.

His stomach trouble firmly established as a means of handling his conflict and as an escape from both school and military service, it was difficult for him to allow himself to see his symptoms for what they were. It was even more of a task to try to strengthen his personality so that he would have more than symptoms of illness to call upon when a problem faced him. Here was a boy for whom so much had been done that he had had little ability to do for himself, a boy who had little confidence in himself; 'after all, no one thinks I can do anything, if they did they'd let me try.' Still dependent at an age when he should have been able not only to do for himself but to help others, he had neither the confidence nor the ability to work himself out of his difficulties. The importance of letting young people do more and more for themselves and of showing them in this way your confidence in them are things we all have to remember. We are so sure we could do it better, that they could do better with our help, that if we don't help they will fail or be hurt, that we deprive them of the experiences that would increase both their confidence and their skill. No one would think of allowing young people to attempt too much too soon, but provided they are started very young and then given more and more and greater and greater opportunities to do for themselves, the dangers or mistakes which might result from an adult's failure to help them will be few. Their few errors and bumps will be better for them than to have come through unscathed with our help: the failure will not diminish their confidence, for they will be aware of our confidence in their ability to rise above occasional setbacks.

Many girls find the transition from being a tomboy to being very feminine, from thinking Papa wonderful to having eyes for no one but the boy next door, an easy one. Molly didn't. At eighteen her 'I'm all mixed up' was only too obvious and clearly much more significant than the 'nervous stomach' which she had at first said was her problem.

At various times all through her life she had been bothered by what she called a 'nervous stomach.' When she started off in the first grade, food 'gagged' her. The next summer when her father insisted that she take swimming lessons (he had almost drowned the year before and now refused to go near the water) her stomach acted up again. When she was seven years old her mother died.

All through school she found it impossible to eat when examinations were due, and during her first month away at college she 'couldn't eat a thing.' She had never stopped to think that all these upsets were due to anxiety, but in talking about them she remembered things that had made these times more frightening than they usually would have been: her older sister's tales of what they do at school to little girls who don't behave, her father's near drowning, her father's stern and frequent reminders that college was very expensive and 'it wasn't my idea anyway' and 'you'd better do well or you'll come home.'

What was it that was frightening Molly now? 'Well, I might as well get it over with — I haven't been able to talk to anyone, I'm so mixed up I don't know where to start. It's this man . . .' Ever since she had been a little girl she had adored her father despite his gruffness and rebuffs. She wanted to be like him — or perhaps like her older brother. Girls were silly, parties a waste of time. If she could only be a great swimmer like her brother and then later a lawyer like her father. When she began to mature she had severe pains with her periods — 'I don't know why; I didn't want to get out of anything; as a matter of fact it made me mad that I had them.' All through high school she went to every athletic affair and not a single dance. Attractive, she was invited frequently at first but soon boys stopped trying.

And then, in her second year of college, it happened. 'He's not like those college boys who come up every week end. He's more like my father. Yes, he's a good deal older than I am but that isn't important to me, though some of my friends keep harping on it. But I'm not sure. I like him, but I don't think I want to marry him; I don't think I want to marry anyone. He's nice to me and I don't want to hurt his feelings. I just can't make up my mind. *It makes me sick* to think about it, and it's got my father so upset that I avoid saying anything.'

Some of us apparently are little troubled by the loss of a parent, by threats of the dire things that may happen, or by frightening experiences. But many of us are, and those who are so constituted may find it difficult to manage these together with such matters as becoming feminine and at the same time adjusting their feelings toward the parent of the opposite sex. For adults to be aware of these factors in young people's development is the first step toward helping them: the next is to see that they have the appropriate sort of adult friends. Anxious, confused, and unable to untangle her mixed feelings and fears, the whole situation had become more than Molly could stomach. She needed an opportunity to talk out these feelings of hers, and she needed professional help in understanding them and herself; and while she was doing this and developing more mature attitudes she needed sympathetic support.

Relief from anxiety requires that boys or girls put their upsetting feelings into their own words. When this has been done they will gradually be able to understand what has been going on within themselves and will be able to make a conscious decision regarding their conflict. This is not only a therapeutic but also a maturing experience, for in contrast to their conflicting feelings, it belongs in the adult world: it is an adult rather than a childish way of meeting a problem. In their early years neither individuals nor nations put their feelings into words; they cry and strike out, without discussing, against whatever seems hostile or mysterious. It is only with maturity that feeling is transferred from thoughtless action into words and understanding. Now these feelings, and the conflicts they threaten to arouse, are no longer met with irresolution, and the adolescent is no longer torn between siding with either mother or father; no longer will the boy or girl fear condemnation and retribution from the one they reject; no longer do they fear growing up or assuming an adult's responsibilities. Whatever the outcome, their anxiety, since there is no longer an unknown and nameless conflict within them, will be largely resolved.

By giving names to phenomena, we too often pretend to have solved their mystery. The different forms of anxiety are a case in point. There is so much to learn about them that each has been given a name. *Phobia* is one of these. It is, of course, no more than the Greek word for *fear*, and when it is better understood perhaps this classical name will be discarded and it may be called *unreasoning fear*, for such it is. It often has an element of anger too. When, for instance, a schoolboy's fear of an examination is entirely unreasonable and unjustified, what appears to be fear may in reality be anger.

Tom sought help because he invariably vomited on getting up in the morning on days when quizzes or examinations were scheduled. During an exam he would shake and sweat copiously; his thinking would be confused. Though well prepared, he usually failed miserably.

When he was encouraged to talk about his difficulty he was

at first unable to say anything about it save to describe his symptoms. Later as he continued to talk he told that in an examination he had the feeling that he was a criminal who was being tried by a judge. Tom knew that he felt guilty about something but what it was he could not say at first. He said that he had felt much the same in coming for help, and he openly expressed feelings of anger and resentment toward his doctor. That he should feel this way baffled him until he realized that his doctor reminded him of one of his teachers and, more significantly, of his father.

Once Tom had started to talk about his father it was as if a long and violent outpouring of anger had been released. He told how his father had 'deserted' him and his mother when he was eleven, and how before this his relationship to his father had been a long series of false hopes and broken promises. Later it was suggested to him that his feeling of guilt in examinations might be due to his own dim awareness of the unfairness of his being angry at his blameless teacher, who not only was *not* his father but also differed considerably from him. Tom accepted this suggestion with great relief: he had bottled up his anger and resentment, and now that he had at long last put his feelings into words his symptoms gradually decreased.

Not all the upsets which examinations bring are related to fear of the tests themselves. School is an emotion-charged situation, where not infrequently teachers are associated in their pupils' minds with other adults whom they may either admire or dislike. Often these feelings have little apparent effect, but for some adolescents they may be the factor which determines success or failure. The important things to remember are that such feelings do exist, that in the classroom there is not just an intellectual, but also an emotional interchange. At times a good relationship with a teacher results in a mediocre student's exceptional success, whereas a poor relationship may account for an excellent mind's inefficiency at school.

The tension which anxiety produces commonly causes boys

and girls to forget the material they have studied for an examination. Amnesia is like this: it is just a more severe form of forgetting. A boy or girl who has amnesia may forget his own name and whereabouts, and may go away from home as if escaping some dreadful threat. He is in fact doing just that, except that what he fears and is trying to escape is within himself. When such a flight is as unfounded in reason as is a phobia's fear, it is called a fugue.

To understand the nature of amnesia, it is necessary to remember the changes in feeling that occur during adolescence. In addition to a return to a state of self-love and preoccupation with himself, the adolescent boy is in the throes of diminishing his urges to be like his mother, of increasing his masculine behavior, and of rebelling against his father. The adolescent girl is relinquishing her tomboyishness, is breaking from her father, and is becoming increasingly feminine. These changes are not always easily or smoothly achieved. New feelings bring new responsibilities; the severing of old ties and the development of new ones are not painless.

For some adolescents it can be very confusing, and when these emotional changes run up against a complicating factor, amnesia may be the result. It is as though the situation was so intolerable that to forget everything seems to be the only way out. Amnesia may develop, for instance, if a boy has developed an intense attachment for another boy or teacher or club leader. The homosexual cast of such a relationship excites intense anxiety. In the midst of trying to adjust to the usual changes in feeling which occur during these years, this boy is faced with the impossible task of understanding feelings which stem from self-love, from what is left of his desire to be feminine like his mother, from the attraction for whatever of the feminine exists in the boy or teacher or club leader, and in part from the masculine part of his own nature.

Bill was a personable eighteen-year-old when he was thrown into the exciting experience of college fraternity life as a freshman pledge. He had been, as an only child, close to his father and even closer to his mother but had not, to all outward appearances, adopted any of her feminine traits. Into the highly masculine atmosphere of the fraternity house he found himself very much drawn to the companionship of one other young fellow who was as near the 'all-American' model as one could hope to find. Their friendship, which at first started on a superficial level, gradually deepened until Bill became so powerfully involved in his fondness for his fraternity brother that he began to be deeply upset. The nature of this disturbance was not apparent to Bill and only showed itself by an inability to sleep as soundly as he had formerly, a loss of interest in food, and a considerable amount of impairment in his powers of concentration and thinking.

One evening Bill disappeared. When he was picked up three days later in another city, quite unkempt, he had no recollection of what he had done in the intervening time and was completely bewildered by the whole affair. His parents and the school authorities had been very much troubled by this outburst — a typical hysterical fugue, initiated by the intensity of the friendship between Bill and his fraternity brother.

Once put into words, every tension growing out of incomprehensible feelings or situations too difficult for the person to solve loses its power to confuse or to necessitate such an escape as amnesia or fugue. To prevent the development of such tensions, one thinks of the importance of wider friendships rather than an excessively close attachment to a single member of one's own sex, the value of activities which widen one's circle of acquaintances and bring satisfaction and recognition, and the need for all of us to be more aware of the mechanisms of these difficulties so that we may earlier get at their causes.

Forms of hysteria such as paralyses of limbs are not uncommon in adolescence. They develop when emotion is repressed and is subsequently shunted into a limb, causing it to be paralyzed; so also can a situation from which the adolescent sees no other means of escape.

Sam's childhood had not been a very happy one. At eight a long and painful illness confined him to a hospital for several months, and just as he was getting well war broke out and his father left home to enter the navy. For several years Sam and his mother and his older sister were alone. He didn't mind this too much, for his father had seemed very annoyed by his illness and his mother was very kind and patient.

The war over, Sam's father came home. He had always wanted a son who would be a great athlete; Sam's illness made him feel that Sam would never be strong. But he hadn't expected to find him so small and frail and so much more interested in music than in baseball and football. That was too much, and without saying anything to his wife or to Sam he entered the boy in a boarding school 'where they knew the importance of athletics and where they'd make a man of him.' Sam went — there was nothing else he could do — and he was utterly miserable. He had neither the strength nor the skill nor the interest to do well at games. His studies were hard and left him no time for music. People were nice enough to him, in fact went out of their way to make him happy, but he felt like a fish out of water. At Christmas time he begged his father to let him stay home and got no more than being called a quitter and a sissy. His mother was sympathetic but had been told that it had been her nonsense that had spoiled the boy in the first place. There seemed to be no way out.

While Sam was packing his trunk to go back to school, the catch slipped and the lid fell on his arm. His 'ouch' brought his mother running, and though it really didn't hurt him much, he didn't seem to be able to raise his arm or move his fingers. The accident, the doctor's visit, the X-rays, the long and fruitless search for the cause of the persistent paralysis, did more than defer Sam's return to school. Out of it all his father finally came to realize what he was up against, why he felt as he did, and what Sam, with all his assets and liabilities, was like. And Sam, now out of his dilemma, gradually found his arm improving and willingly acquired a better understanding of himself, of his father, and of why he really failed to get along at boarding school. Hysteria is hardly an ideal way to solve a difficult situation, but if its treatment leads to a better understanding of one's own and one's parents' personalities and needs, it is far from a total loss.

An ex-marine, on his return to college under the GI Bill, also presented an interesting though less typical example of hysteria. He had made many island landings in the South Pacific campaign, including Tarawa, but he seemed unable to take even his daily tests in his stride. On going into a quiz he would have feelings almost identical with those he remembered having on the way to a beachhead. It was as though he mobilized for a little daily test all the aggressive impulses he had needed to bring himself to kill an enemy. Years of combat had accustomed him to treating every kind of emergency as a battle situation. But now in an examination, instead of an M-30 carbine to protect himself, he had only a pen, and in his mind it plainly did not seem mightier than his gun. Trying to maintain his hero status in the halls of learning, and finding that his long absence from study now demanded every bit of concentration, he went into an examination teeming with aggression. But at this beachhead there was no living enemy to combat, just an impassive examination sheet relentlessly shooting one question after another at him. Fortunately, in talking about his situation he could see the humor in it, and his colorful vocabulary let loose his strong feelings in a very helpful fashion. Before long he had seen the hopelessness in using his marine methods in fighting examinations, and made his readjustment to civilian life.

We are all familiar with schoolboy slang. Many of their words are packed with aggression. 'Knocked it for a loop,' 'socked it,' 'knocked it cold' — all hint at the pugnacious attitude that adolescents take toward studies. Such attitudes provide an outlet for our powerful aggressive impulses. Athletics are another outlet, but even with these two, under some circumstances and with some people, enough aggression may be repressed to cause a build-up of anxiety-provoking tensions.

Adults can do much to alleviate these tensions. Even though the more maladjusted adolescent may have developed only limited outlets, at least the most effective one — speech — is ready for his intensive use. By encouraging young people to express their feelings and by giving them other appropriate outlets, much can be done to prevent the development of excessive tensions.

Adolescents are in the throes of building their own personalities, of trying to become the sort of person they feel they want to be. They want at the same time to please their parents, to get their praise and approval. When, like Sam, they find that they are utterly unacceptable to one or both parents and believe that they are unsuited by temperament, interests, or skill to be what either or both parents seem to want and to admire, they have a real dilemma, and not a few develop some sort of anxiety state. By no means do all adolescents have a clear or the best idea of what they want to do with their lives, or a correct assessment of their potentialities; but on the other hand some parents, like Sam's father, make decisions which are based on their own feelings rather than on their children's capabilities or personalities. Perhaps their greatest error is that they forget that adolescents are people, not puppets to be moved at will — that they are people desperately trying, at this stage of their development, to build their own personalities, live their own lives. The adult, be he parent or coach or teacher, who stops to think and who pauses to analyze his own feelings, will try to guide and won't try to force into a mold, won't behave as does the dictator.

VII

Psychosomatic Disorders

Psychosomatic illnesses are frequent among adolescents, but
the reason for a persistent or a frequently recurring symptom — headache, backache, nausea, diarrhea, palpitation —
is often difficult to determine. Obviously, first there should be
an attempt to determine whether some physical ailment is
responsible for the symptom, while at the same time remembering that physical disorders usually have an emotional component. Most of us feel sorry for ourselves when a bad cold
or influenza confines us to bed. We enjoy, without openly

admitting it, the many attentions we receive at such times. We enjoy being babied and, although we would resent being told so, our emotional state at such times is not far removed from the fussy impatience of the helpless child. This is our chance to go back emotionally to a childhood level and to enjoy behaving like someone little and helpless. All this is a common accompaniment of organic illness. Often, however, the emotions do much more than accompany: they actually produce a physical disturbance, a symptom resembling those in a sickness. It is our emotions which produce the dry lips, the moist hands, and the sinking feeling in the pit of the stomach which is the personal experience of most of us when we stand to address an audience.

When an adolescent varies from his or her companions in rate of maturing, emotional difficulties, changes in behavior, and a falling off in studies may occur. During his late childhood and his early adolescence Ted had been exceptionally healthy and happy; he had had many friends and had done well in junior high school. He started off well at fifteen in his first year of senior high school, but before Thanksgiving he was having headaches, his irritability and moodiness were very noticeable, and he was doing poorly at school. At first his parents thought he was just temporarily having trouble in adjusting to the big high school. His teachers, who had not known him as he used to be, assured his parents that this sort of thing often happened and that undoubtedly it would straighten out. By mid-December, however, they weren't so sure, complained that he couldn't seem to concentrate, and suggested to Ted's parents that unless things changed for the better, it would be well for him to have a thorough physical check-up during the Christmas vacation period. There wasn't any improvement. As a matter of fact things got worse. Ted spent more and more time in his room, apparently studying, but his marks went down. He complained of feeling tired. Despite urging he refused to reconsider his decision not to try out for the swimming team: swimming had been his favorite sport and he had been very successful at it. He didn't go to any school dances. At mealtime Ted often seemed preoccupied, answered in monosyllables, and clearly resented any questions about how he felt or what was the matter.

When Ted's mother telephoned their doctor for an appointment, sensing the situation, he mentioned an evening when he would have plenty of time and suggested that Ted come in alone. 'He's old enough to go to his doctor by himself; we'll do better if you'll just leave it to him.' At first Ted said little. He answered the doctor courteously enough, but he didn't volunteer anything: it was as though he were sizing up the situation and the doctor. He watched the doctor intently, apparently was weighing each of the doctor's few comments, and seemed to be trying to make up his mind. The tip-off came at the start of the physical examination when Ted was casually asked to 'hop on the scales and we'll get you weighed and measured.' He didn't 'hop'; his slow step, his hanging head were all the doctor needed to confirm his guess that what was bothering him was his failure to grow and to mature. It wasn't that he couldn't concentrate; it was that he couldn't stop concentrating on this thing that worried him. It was this that made him irritable, that gave him a headache.

'Am I ever going to grow? Why am I so short? Is it because I masturbate — that's what one of the fellows said. I don't have any hair or anything — they make fun of me. I wasn't going to say anything to you. I will grow, won't I?' Getting all this off his chest helped a great deal. Once he had finally dared to come out with it, he talked freely. Then reassurance, the feeling that someone was sharing his problem, and a chance to learn about how perfectly normal people vary from one another in the way they grow — all these helped. And Ted gradually lost his headaches and his irritability and was again able to concentrate on his studies.

Few adolescents are aware that wide variation from the

average is compatible with normality. To most of them, to vary from what is average is to be abnormal. We need to convince them that a variety of different states and rates of development really are normal, and to do this we must ourselves have a basic understanding of the facts of growth.

Those studies of somatic growth which have involved the observation of the same adolescents over a period of several years have permitted generalizations which are of great value. Data based on the height or weight or state of maturity of members of a given group at a single point in time are helpful, but information which is of much more valid application to an individual adolescent's growth problem is obtained from the year-after-year study of the growth patterns of the same boys and girls. From such material one learns to have great respect for individual differences in rate and time and extent of growing. Even though boys and girls are perfectly normal and free from chronic illness or nutritional disturbance, they will vary widely from one another in their mode and extent of growth. If adolescents have anything in common, it would appear to be that each has his own individual growth pattern — that each differs from the other.

Growth is not even and orderly. Rates of growth are best shown in charts which plot the year-by-year increments in height. Such charts clearly show that the rate of growth is not steady, that the rate of growth is by far the greatest during the early months of life, that it is slightly accelerated between the ages of six and eight, and markedly accelerated at some point between the ages of twelve and sixteen, a phenomenon which is usually referred to as the adolescent growth spurt. The adolescent growth spurt occurs in all boys and girls, but the age at which it appears, its extent, and its duration vary considerably from one individual to another. In boys it usually occurs between the ages of twelve and sixteen. It may result in an increase of from four to twelve inches in height, and produces, on the average, an increase of about four inches in height within a year. In girls the adolescent growth spurt begins earlier, commonly occurring between eleven and fourteen, and usually proceeds at a somewhat slower rate and to a lesser extent than in boys.

All parts of the body increase at this time, but all parts of the body do not grow to the same degree at the same time. Leg length increases first and is usually first to complete its spurt. The hips widen before the shoulders. The increase in trunk length and increase in chest depth comes later. The major increase in muscle and weight tends to come last. Subcutaneous fat, particularly in boys, is apt to show a considerable increase before the height spurt develops. A year or two later this fat is lost and tends to recur only when the skeletal growth spurt has subsided. In boys usually one sees a gradual increase in size of genitalia, then the appearance and development of pubic, facial, then axillary hair. In girls, one first notices a budding of the breasts, next an appearance of pubic hair, and then the menarche. The timing, their sequence, and the extent of these vary among individuals. They are important straws in the wind, however, when, for instance, a boy whose present height is at the lower limits of normal height shows evidence of growth in his leg length; or, when seeming immature, pubic hair begins to develop: these are reassuring signs and indicate that the growth phenomena of adolescence are beginning to emerge.

A measurement taken on an adolescent at a single point in time has little meaning. Two successive measurements mean more; three, a great deal. It is an adolescent's *progress* toward a desirable state — not how one finds him at a single point in time — that is important. Adolescence is not static; it is a process. That *change* is occurring in some one of these aspects of growth suggests that the usual and further changes in other respects will soon appear. It is when no change is taking place and when the skeletal age is far advanced beyond the time for such changes that one should suspect that something is wrong.

Although we constantly refer to age when discussing these matters of growth, it is important to keep in mind that chronological age can be very deceptive during the adolescent years. Skeletal or developmental age is a much more accurate yardstick to use when one is trying to judge or to describe how 'grown up' an adolescent is. These 'ages' are based on the state of the bones' development or on the state to which such secondary sexual characteristics as pubic and axillary hair have progressed. These are much more realistic indicators of a boy's or girl's actual degree of maturity than is the number of birthdays each has had. To put it briefly, when you talk about boys all of whom have a skeletal or developmental age of fifteen, you are talking about boys all of whom have advanced to just about the same point in bone development and sexual maturity. On the other hand, a group of boys whose chronological age is fifteen vary tremendously from one another in the degree to which they have developed toward physical maturity. At chronological age fifteen, boys and girls may vary all the way from less than thirteen years to more than seventeen years in skeletal or developmental age.

Normal, healthy individuals show wide differences in various growth phenomena. The vast majority of them reach a satisfactory and what may well be for each of them an ideal adult state, though their ways of reaching that goal may vary considerably. Though these are facts, and though the individual would do well, except in rare instances, to accept himself as he is and not wish to imitate some standard pattern, adults should recognize the psychological potentialities of wide differences from the usual and anticipate the anxieties which are so likely to develop in adolescents who find themselves different. Furthermore it is one thing to understand that these differences frequently occur and are within normal limits, and quite another thing to ignore them and to forget that they can be the source of real anxiety and of a variety of psychosomatic disorders. In dealing with adolescents, it is therefore necessary to appreciate how much they dislike being different and how anxious they may become when they believe they are abnormal, and to have constantly in our own minds not average data and chronological age standards but instead a clear picture of the wide variations which are still well within normal limits.

To assume that symptoms have an emotional cause, no matter how clear it is that there are emotional factors in the situation, is dangerous unless there has first been a *thorough* search for physical disorders. Signs and symptoms vary within a wide range and often demand the physician's closest scrutiny. Only a well-trained physician should attempt to distinguish between the organic and emotional elements of headaches, peptic ulcer, ulcerative colitis, migraine, asthma, backaches, enuresis, vomiting, paralysis, disturbance of vision and hearing, and other symptoms which may be due to either organic or emotional disturbance. Even when it is clear that a symptom is largely emotional in origin, that symptom or a new physical complaint requires careful medical diagnostic study during the course of any treatment designed to correct the patient's upset emotions.

Judy had had a physical examination, but because she had so many behavior problems no one paid much attention to her physical well-being, and her examination was perfunctory. She was destructive, she refused to do her schoolwork, she was insolent. Formerly she had been friendly, but now she was antagonistic. She refused to eat, her plumpness had been lost and she had become alarmingly thin. Her parents seemed to be very gentle and affectionate and only the information that no physical ailment was present enabled them to listen to the psychologist's explanation that it was her hostile feelings toward them that were the reasons for her destroying things they had given her and for her refusing to accept their advice or their food. Logical as that explanation might have been for many such thirteen-year-old girls or boys whose behavior was similar to Judy's, her parents couldn't quite believe it, and before following out the recommendation that she be given intensive psychotherapy they decided that they wanted a medical examination. In this instance they were wise; and no doubt any psychiatrist would have insisted on a more extensive physical survey than she had had. A fresh approach, and doubtless because now later in the illness the signs were more apparent, revealed a very different situation. The girl's very dry skin, emaciation, coarse hair, thin eyebrows, all suggested hypothyroidism and subsequent laboratory tests bore out this diagnosis. At that time she told her doctor of her former unhappiness in having been a 'fat girl,' the consequent teasing, her resentment of it, and her decision to lose weight. Wanting to eat, wanting to be friendly, she had clearly been at war with herself.

Whether Judy's hypothyroidism was coincident with, or caused by, or followed by malnutrition, one can only speculate. We do know that she rapidly improved after she was given glandular therapy; she began to eat, gained weight and strength, and again became her happy, friendly self. Medical factors or causes are not to be slighted just because emotional ones are present.

Though it is physicians who have the training to follow the medical aspects of disease and though they or psychiatrists are best fitted to relieve the patient's emotional tensions, it is well for everyone to have some awareness of the nature of psychosomatic illnesses. Many psychosomatic diseases, if treated early in their course, would never become the chronic cases so refractory to treatment that we now often see in hospitals. Parents, teachers, counselors, and club leaders, by giving attention to illnesses and by insisting that they be seen by a physician, will save endless suffering and permit a much higher percentage of people to be helped. To tell a boy or girl to 'buck up' or 'forget it' when you don't know the reason for his symptoms, or when you only suspect they have emotional basis, is far from helpful.

Whatever the emotional causes may be, the development of a bodily illness laden with emotional factors produces in reality a form of regressive behavior: a kind of behavior which resembles and re-enacts that of childhood. It is made all the more pernicious and difficult to change because it has an accompanying physical excuse which evokes sympathy from many and which seems to justify one's giving up the life struggle and again becoming a helpless child who must be cared for.

Why this kind of illness appears in some people and not in others has become clearer as we have learned more about the way it develops. Those of us who since childhood have been able to give expression to deep feelings are less likely to develop a psychosomatic disease. This is a safety valve which a patient suffering from a psychosomatic illness apparently lacks, so it is in the younger years that the groundwork seems to have been laid for the future onset of this kind of illness. In adult life we may be more open in our zeal or expressions of anger at injustice, but it is the roots of these feelings which cause trouble: they go back to early life when we were unable to say what we felt.

Usually a patient who has, for example, an ulcer, speaks out freely certain of his feelings; but others, deeper buried and long pent up, he is unable to put into words. So instead of putting his emotions into words this patient 'talks' with his body. His powerful emotion is diverted from expression through the nerves, muscles, and organs of speech into those of the stomach and bowel, and there they cause pain, discomfort, and physical changes. All of us have had a similar reaction at a time when fright makes us speechless and we are temporarily unable to express our fear in words. But our vegetative nervous system expresses it for us; our hair stands on end, our pupils dilate, and our hearts beat rapidly.

Those are the mechanics of these disorders as we understand them. The less severe and the more common psychosomatic ailments which plague adolescents arise and behave in a similar manner. Joe had seemed preoccupied and tired during the last month of school. As soon as his eighth grade was over, his mother took him for a physical check-up. She told the doctor (he was a stranger to them; they had moved to this town within a year) all about Joe and waited for his report. All the while Joe sat apprehensive and a bit sullen and did no more than make monosyllabic replies. When examined he was sweating profusely and his heart rate was very rapid. Tests to determine whether or not heart disease or rheumatic fever were present were suggested to his mother, and it was advised that he 'take it very easy and not exert himself.' Taking it easy is hardly what a thirteen-year-old boy has looked forward to as his summer vacation's program, and Joe became increasingly hard to live with. The doctor's later report had not been at all positive — it merely said that Joe 'might have some trouble' and had better have further tests.

When the time for his next appointment came, his mother was ill so Joe went off to the doctor's office alone. It was a much more satisfactory visit for both of them. Alone, unembarrassed by his mother's presence, with the chance to tell his own story and to answer the doctor's questions himself, things went very well. There had been little in Joe's examination to suggest heart disease, and the doctor suspected that the sweating and rapid heart rate might be due to anxiety. 'Your masturbation got you worried, Joe?' was all that was needed to bring out his 'Is it as bad for you as Dad said? Will it really stop you growing? Is that why my face is broken out? How can I stop thinking about Miss Moon, I don't mean to — she's my teacher —

but I can't stop — I was scared you'd find out and say something in front of my mother.'

Nothing can cause the adolescent more apprehension or arouse more feelings of guilt than can sex. Masturbation, their feelings toward the opposite sex, their unanswered questions, their fear of discovery, their uncertainty as to what to believe, the conflict between their behavior and thoughts and what they see and hear of adults' conduct and what they have been told was good or right — these confuse and upset them. Their conflicts not only preoccupy them but also give rise to anxiety, which in turn produces those common accompaniments of fear — sweating and rapid heart rate.

Many girls find adolescence no less difficult than do boys, and during this transition period old troubles may become accentuated or new ones may appear. Edith had always been a worrier. Despite her very high marks her hands would shake when she was given her report card and she would dread being asked to take part in a special school program that involved her speaking to an audience. At ten she had been in a serious automobile accident and after that every time she heard brakes screech she would feel 'trembly all over,' and her heart would pound. Edith's mother gave her everything — all her time and attention and solicitude. She was always asking Edith if she was tired and telling her not to overdo. Her father had long been an invalid and when Edith was six his heart disease was fatal.

Edith's old worries were now compounded by her mother's fears and extreme oversolicitude. Moreover, she was confused in her feelings toward growing up. At times she wanted to be like her father, a doctor; one day she had no thought except for the boy next door, the next she 'couldn't stand him'; she dreaded her math class — 'Mr. Sutton frightens me — I hate him'; and yet she refused offers to transfer her to another teacher. One day she would refuse to accept her mother's suggestion that she select her own clothes and the next she would talk of nothing but her desire to escape from her mother's domination. In the midst of this vacillation between wanting to be feminine and fearing to be, and wanting to be free of her mother and lacking confidence in her ability to be, the need arose for her to make a decision about her future schooling. Should she go to college; should she go to a local college and stay with her lonely mother or should she break away and enter a school far away; should she plan for a career in medicine or just go on with her education for cultural reasons? The result of every test in school bore on these questions, so each one found her more anxious than the last. By the time her college entrance examinations were imminent, she was so upset that her mother insisted that she must be ill.

A perfectly normal physical examination (when we discounted her excessive sweating and rapid heart rate) was in strong contrast with her long list of symptoms. 'There's a tight feeling in my chest — it's as though someone were sitting on me' was the worst, most recent, and the most revealing one.

Edith had some of the symptoms of mild heart disease and none of the physical signs. She was clearly suffering from her worries and conflicts, old and new. Some of them could be relieved quickly, but to get her straightened out and ready to live happily and efficiently took quite a bit of time. She said that talking about her feelings about leaving her mother, about her reasons for wanting to be a doctor and about her real reasons for thinking boys 'silly' and girls who pursued them 'disgusting,' helped to get 'quite a load off my chest.' At any rate, it was possible to help her through a period of uncertainty and enable her to meet daily tasks with less anxiety.

Treatment should be given early and before years of living with a symptom have fixed it firmly. Much depends upon early recognition and prompt treatment. Bill told his doctor that he had had a pain over his heart for three months and that none of the physicians he had consulted could find anything wrong with his heart. His description of his pain was indeed suggestive of heart disease, but since the physical examination of his heart, his electrocardiogram, and heart X-rays were all perfectly normal, there was little reason to believe that his pain had an organic basis.

In his initial interview Bill said that his symptoms had begun on Christmas Eve. Later he explained that he had arrived home from school for the holidays on that day, and that on Christmas Day his father had a heart attack and had died within a few hours. From this it seemed most likely that his symptoms were a form of deep grieving, and so every effort was made to have him express as much feeling as he could about his dead father. Within a few days he was practically free of his symptoms. Apparently the long-forgotten feelings he had had toward his father, and the guilt such feelings had caused him, had been quickly eliminated.

Such a prompt response to treatment is uncommon but there is every reason to believe that a great deal of severe psychosomatic disease would be equally quickly ameliorated if patients could only be seen early, that is at most within two or three months of the onset of their symptoms. Early in the course of the psychosomatic illness the personality has not undergone the marked changes or built the defenses that develop when it has long persisted. Later, when the symptoms are firmly established, it is as if the entire personality had reformed around the disease process; it acts as if *that* were the core structure about which the patient's lowered efficiency and avoidance of life as an adult revolved.

Dysmenorrhea, menstrual cramps, is common. But just because it is common is no reason for ignoring this symptom. The *cause* of severe, incapacitating cramps — cramps which keep a girl out of school or activities — ought to be investigated. It is not the symptom itself, but the possible causes which make us pay heed to them. Only rarely will the cause be organic, that is, due to such things as a cyst or adhesions; but a girl who has this symptom ought first to have a thorough physical examination. Often, however, our task will be to find out what this symptom is saying: in this case what is it that has her keyed up and tense, what is it that 'gripes' her. Many will need just a little attention — but that 'little attention' may be more helpful than one would suspect. Others need more help to straighten out their worries, their sources of tension. Here again we think of the things that worry girls who are growing up, who are about to become women. These aren't the matters which bother little children — or adults. It's more likely to be things like school, or death, or wanting to be a boy, or sex, or a poor relationship with her mother. These young people need a chance to get these matters straight before they develop into firmly fixed attitudes: now, not in adulthood, is the time to get at them.

When Mary was thirteen, her periods were so painful that she would go to bed with nausea and cramps for at least a day. Her physical examination revealed nothing of importance except that she gave the impression of being a very proper, very tense little girl. She was the eldest of eight children and clearly the serious, responsible one. She said she disliked boys, didn't care for parties, didn't like to get 'dressed up.'

At first Mary was reluctant to talk, but gradually, as though she had begun to realize that someone was really interested in her — not just in her symptoms — she began to lose some of her prim, inhibited ways, complained of her many duties at home, and hinted at her resentment of her 'lucky brothers.' Once Mary had dared to say some of these things, she began to talk more freely, and as she let herself go, her cramps became less severe and her appearance less rigid and plain. She began to dress up a little, had a date or two (timidly, for her mother had warned her time and time again to 'watch out for boys'), and finally came in with a new dress, a new hair-do, and the news that she had a boy friend. The last had perhaps been a little too much for her, for her cramps, which had all but disappeared, now returned! However, the conflicts which her feelings about her boy friend had aroused were straightened out very shortly, and we can predict with some certainty that those fears, resentments, and desires which confuse and up-set some girls as they grow up will no longer disturb Mary.

What can adults do to lessen the chance that a child or an adolescent will develop a real psychosomatic disorder? The importance of an emotionally secure upbringing cannot be stressed too much. Well-adjusted parents who have them-selves under control, who have their own satisfying lives, usu-ally produce children like themselves, tolerant, flexible, stable. A well-balanced but active home is the best insurance against future emotional troubles for the children who grow up in it. With this sort of start in life, later unavoidable experiences which might otherwise be harsh emotional shocks will be taken in stride.

Adults often thoughtlessly provide young children with a model of behavior that will later blossom into a psychosomatic illness in adolescence. A mother who invariably develops a headache, backache, or some other discomfort when an un-welcome visitor comes or when she is faced with something she doesn't want to do is setting an example for her children that may produce similar symptoms under like circumstances in them. Young children are great imitators: the behavior of elders they love may be reproduced in miniature by them, at times in a most embarrassing fashion. This is one of the ways that the seeds of a future psychosomatic illness may be sown although adults are rarely aware that it is happening.

Adults' attitudes toward real illness — as well as their use of symptoms as an excuse — are important too. Illnesses are to be treated objectively, not feared; a cut or a sprain is to be treated, not just talked about and worried over.

Children can't be protected forever from frightening experiences, but they can be prepared for them. One does not hope forever to spare them, but only that they may first be made ready to meet these insults and later only gradually have to take them on. None of us really believes that throwing a child into open water is the way to teach him to swim. Little children who have not been made fearful and anxious by the daily uncertainties and unpredictable behavior around them rarely fear such an experience as going to a hospital: adults have been kind and thoughtful to them and they have no reason to think doctors and nurses will be otherwise. To the insecure, overanxious child they are mysterious and fearful strangers, and indeed some of them, because of quirks in their own personalities, may thoughtlessly do or say things jokingly to ease the child's own discomfort which will be taken as fact and increase their anxiety. We can easily underestimate how frightening hospitalization can be. It is not unusual to have an adolescent recall an early hospital experience in vivid detail. Fifteen years later Sam remembered his tonsillectomy at five. 'The doctor was very nice to me — he was a big man with a mustache. I remember his taking my hand when we went up a big staircase. Then he went away. Later they wheeled me down the hall. There was a tight sheet over me and I couldn't move at all. People were always coming in and looking at me and then going away as though they were looking for someone else. Then I remember someone putting something over my face. I kept trying to see it and couldn't and it sort of smothered me.' We can only speculate as to the relationship of this experience to the facial tic which annoyed him so many years afterward, but it is not difficult to believe that an experience so vividly recalled many years later is capable of causing such a symptom.

The first hospitalization is but one of many experiences that can later cause trouble. Unpleasantness in starting out at school, an unexpected vicious attack on the street, or other frightening experiences in early childhood may be more than the child is prepared to withstand. Many of these cannot be avoided. We can, however, keep in mind the possibility that a bodily complaint could have an emotional cause, and do our best to see to it that help is offered early.

VIII

Homesickness

At the opening of a school in the fall, or of a camp in the summer, a new crop of youngsters arrives. They are eager, apprehensive, and tense with the excitement of a new adventure and inwardly stirred by the breaking of ties with those at home. This break with home almost always rouses mixed feelings in the adolescent. On the one hand he is struggling for independence — cutting the apron strings; on the other, old needs stir within him and he swings to a greater dependence than ever on his bewildered parents. All this is typical of the

adolescent whose desire and capacity for independence vacillate between those of a man and a mouse: it echoes the period
of negativism so common in the three-year-old who says 'No!'
to everything in his first attempts to build up the boundaries
of his own expanding personality.

Going out into the new life of camp or school furnishes
nourishing, though at times temporarily indigestible, food for
the independence-seeking youth. Most adolescents welcome
the new adventure. The real threats of strangeness are for the
boy or girl who is insecure, whose early years failed to develop
a sturdy personality. The ties with home, with friends, with
childhood irresponsibility, with the familiar streets and lawns
and dogs, the family cat and the mailman are being severed.
Now one suddenly is unable to find one's way about hallways
in the dark; now one's worth must be proved to strangers. For
the first time acceptance no longer depends on long and un-
critical familiarity. To some this brings homesickness.

The bonds of feeling which cement a family together have
various qualities. These depend for the most part on the characteristics of each parent's personality. When the father is
firm but strong, a man whose gruffness all but hides his deep
and sensitive fondness for his children, his sons are likely to
show a strong wish to copy his manner of doing things, and
his daughters are apt to develop a love that is warm and feminine. Such a man develops solid feelings of security in his
children which later allow their parting from home to be a
new and exciting experience. At their going away little feeling
will appear to be directed toward the folks they have left
behind, but it will be a happy, confident departure with more
feeling than they have the capacity to express.

This father may have as his wife a warm, steady, feminine
woman perhaps a little in the background but always there,
always to be relied upon. She welcomed the arrival of each
baby and surrounded each with the loving kindness of true
motherhood while not neglecting her older children. She gave

to each of her children those feelings of inner security that will permit them confidently and eagerly to venture when the powerful surges of puberty stir their marrow.

From such fine families come the well-adjusted masculine boys and feminine girls who provide us with the standard against which the occasional homesick boy or girl may be compared. Fathers and mothers like those are not as numerous in our present-day urban society as one would wish. True, we can be sure that the great middle class, whether urban or rural, contains great numbers of them. We tend to become pessimistic because it is the less ideal which fill our newspapers and our clinics.

Homesickness, though mild and usually short-lived, is a product of the manner in which the boy or girl was reared in infancy and early childhood and of the emotional climate provided for them by their mothers and fathers. Nostalgia is a longing for the protection and nurture that the home provides. Why does the lust for adventure and new experience so usual in the adolescent boy or girl not overcome this longing, why does it let homesickness develop? Here, perhaps, in miniature is a transitory experience similar to mourning and melancholia. Freud, in one of his most profound theses, postulated an arrest of emotional growth in those who, upon the death of someone dear to them, have become melancholic. For, he said, the self-blame and excess of hatred poured upon his own head by the melancholic is so counter to the natural spirit of man that some deep fault must lie in such a sufferer's development. Natural grief is a gradual healing of the many broken bonds that have been rent by the death of a loved one. The grieving person talks sorrowfully of the many merits of the departed one, and in talking begins to heal the hurt within. In contrast, the melancholic appears sorry for himself, is sunk in a wallow of self-accusation, and protests guilt and unworthiness. Much of a melancholic's guilt appears to come from his vague awareness of the suppressed anger he felt for the loved one who died. Adolescents similarly have anger mixed with their love for those about them. When home is far away and this is recalled, it can produce the feelings of sadness and unworthiness (similar to the self-blame and hatred the melancholic feels) which we call homesickness. When this is the cause of homesickness, clearly its best cure is an opportunity to put those mixed feelings into words. A sympathetic ear, a listener — not an adviser, not silence, not a pep talk — will usually clear up the trouble in short order.

Camp was a grim and lonely place for Bill. This was the first time, though he was fifteen, that he had left Dad and Mother, home, friends, and his dog. His mother had always taken complete charge of him; she had always made all the decisions for him — his clothes, his choice of camp, his appointments for school, the dentist, the barber, and for music lessons. So now he felt lost without her there to decide about things. Now there were no warnings or urgings or invitations especially for him; no one seemed to go out of his way to help him or to include him; the group's routine and announcements were considered enough, as indeed they should have been. Unconsciously waiting for special attention and not getting it, he felt abused and lonely. 'I guess they don't want me. I'm certainly not going to force myself on them.' Somehow he didn't like this camp or the boys there. All he did was think about home and wonder how his dog was and what Dad and Mother and his friends were doing. He blamed himself for not entering into the camp's activities, but in spite of this he just mooned around.

'Maybe I'm going insane. I guess I'd better write my folks and tell them to get me out of here before I go crazy. I'm sure that if I could just get back home I wouldn't go nuts.' Reassurance, attempts at friendliness, pep talks and efforts to get him into things were of no avail. Then he started writing daily cards to his parents. They kept thinking he would get over it, but when he wrote: 'Dear Mom: You'd better take me out

of here before I have a serious mental disease — Love, Bill'
and followed it up with 'Dear Mom — I'm afraid there is no
hope for my mind unless you come and take me home; come
quick, please — Bill' they thought things had gone far enough.
They telegraphed their family physician, who was vacationing
near the camp, to look into the situation. He found Bill with-
drawn and depressed, and at first could get little out of him
except 'I want to go home. I'm no good anyway. I'm sure
I'm going crazy.' Later he was able to get Bill to switch from
talking and thinking about himself to talking about home, his
dog, his parents, what was probably going on there. It took
only a hint or two to get him to talk more about his mother
and soon he was blurting out, 'Why did she send me away?
Why won't she leave me alone?' With enough of his long-
buried anger released and later a chance to put into words his
stifled resentment of his mother's domination, and the chance
to talk to someone about those people and things he had left
behind, his mood gradually changed. He was no longer grim
and without animation. A boy who had really seemed mentally ill was again reacting normally. Given other chances to
talk about things at home, and without being urged to do so,
he gradually entered more and more into camp life. Two weeks
later he was lively and interested in everything.

Homesickness in an adolescent is a temporary regression: it is
not usually a sign of grave illness. He may seem quite depressed, be slow in his speech and answers, and say little except to reiterate 'I want to go home.' In short, he may give
every appearance of having a serious emotional illness; but an
experienced counselor or teacher usually makes a correct evaluation of the severity of the disturbance, and an understanding
listener can usually clear up an attack of nostalgia quickly.

In talking to a homesick boy or girl, one is often surprised
at how little home and loved ones appear in the conversation.

When this is the case, it will help subtly to switch the home-sick boy or girl onto those subjects. The objective is to help these homesick youngsters find words to express the feelings within them. You need to listen rather than talk, but your listening must be accompanied by a balanced and rounded question and comment so that you won't further increase the emotional tension that the boy or girl is feeling: you can rarely accomplish anything with adolescents by adopting a complete silence. Even in the first few minutes of talking they are apt to use old patterns of behavior and feeling that they have used with countless people older than themselves, and which have developed in large part through their original relation-ships with their parents and older brothers and sisters. You must remember that they may respond in this way and behave toward you as they have in the past with their own fathers or mothers.

Your least expression or word will have a profound influence on this talk and on your future relationship with them. If, for example, homesickness is caused by their turning of their anger upon themselves and by feelings of guilt for having ever entertained unnatural feelings toward their parents, it would be reasonable to believe that a stern manner would be most likely to relieve this anger and guilt. However, the homesick adolescent is aware only of sorrow. Good parents have always treated sorrow with kindness and sympathy so these home-sick young people who are behaving at the emotional level of a hurt little child must be treated kindly, not in a severe and punitive manner. At the same time they are not babies, and although their maturity fluctuates widely, talking down to an adolescent will develop savage scorn toward his listener and he will become as silent as the proverbial clam.

Warm sympathy and brief leading questions have to be mixed with enough pause and silence so that the adolescent's feelings will have a chance to flow into speech. This sort of management usually produces the desired result. It relieves the boy of his guilt and sorrow and helps him to get back to normal. Unfortunately, when carried no further, the opportunity for the adolescent to gain new self-understanding is lost. However, the practical demands upon everyone's time, the lack of availability of qualified personnel, and the main business of carrying on school or camp usually make it impossible to take advantage of many opportunities such as these for getting adolescents to understand themselves better. However, when possible, the opportunity should not be thrown away.

Another method of managing homesickness, which at times works miraculously, is the simple, but not always practical expedient of temporarily sending the boy or girl home. The way that Lucy responded to this treatment is revealing. On Monday, the second day of college, she had come to the college physician as forlorn an object as one could imagine. 'Doctor, I've got to go home. I'm no good and this work is way beyond me.' Nothing else would do; she just waited, adamant, for permission to go back to Mother. Daily opportunities to talk did not seem to make up for the attention and affection her parents had given her, and the week end found her unchanged. She still sat silent and forlorn, her eyes cast down, the picture of woe. At this point her parents agreed to the suggestion that she go home for the week end: it was hoped that this might help her out of her despondency. She left on Friday noon, and that same evening she telephoned from home. 'Can I come back to school? I realize what a fool I've been. I'll come back tomorrow so that I can make up the work I've lost.' When she returned next day, animated and eager to get to work, all signs of depression and withdrawal, which had suggested the possibility of a severe mental disorder, were gone. From that time on she was happy and enjoyed her schoolwork and did excellently in it. To give in to a determined and impenetrable insistence on going home, particularly when no progress can be made through efforts to release pent-up feelings, is not necessarily to admit one's failure to help. It can be a very valuable therapeutic device.

A listener need not have professional training in order to help a youngster express pent-up feelings. Most of mankind has lived successfully without the help of psychiatrists, yet few have been able to do without the help a patient and understanding listener gives. We all benefit from having had a good talk with a friend, a minister, a doctor, or anyone who will lend a sympathetic ear. When we are under strong emotional pressure if we will talk, *and use words which have emotional power*, a weight of repression can be lifted and a feeling of great relief will follow.

Certain aids can be used by the inexperienced listener to tide him over those silent periods when he is likely to become uneasy and to say to himself, 'What do I do next?' Obviously it is either because of his own nervousness or conceit if he tries to solve the problem by doing all the talking. The boy or girl he is trying to help will then have little chance to put *his* or *her* feelings into words. Yet a long silence can be most nervewracking to the homesick adolescent. Felix Deutsch years ago devised a method of getting through these trying situations which is of a special value with adolescents. He suggested taking a significant or emotionally laden word which the boy or girl has just used and repeating it in a questioning tone. This can be done without the interviewer introducing a single thought of his own, and it breaks or prevents a threatening silence without interrupting the boy's or girl's train of thought. It is carried out in this fashion:

'Gee, I feel lousy but I don't know what's the matter with me.'

'Lousy?'

'Yes, plain lousy. I don't feel like studying, I can't concentrate. I daydream all the time.'

'You can't concentrate?'

'No, I can't keep my mind on my work; I daydream all the time.'

'Daydream?'

'All I think about is what the guys are doing back home, and what my folks are doing, and my girl.'

'Your girl?'

And so on. Such brief questions which pick up an important and probably emotion-laden word and which do not deflect or interfere with an upset boy's or girl's train of thought are very effective in getting them to express a wealth of feeling. It is a simple technique, but if the interviewer will keep his target constantly in mind, namely, to get feeling expressed, it will be effective. Perhaps never before has this boy or girl been able to put his feelings into words. They may have been pent up since his early childhood when he had no words with which to say them, and surely the restraints of recent years have held them back. Now in an emotional storm they clamor to be spoken against the strong repressive forces which still try to keep them buried. But in a receptive atmosphere, and with the stimulus of these emotionally laden words, the boy or girl will venture a little farther each time, gradually putting more and more feeling into words until at last they'll find themselves effortlessly saying things they had never said before.

Only with considerable training and experience can one expect to discern the emotional significance of all that will be said. Much of it may not have the overtones of feeling for the listener which they have for the speaker: rarely do even simple everyday words have equal significance for two different people. But the voicing of emotion-laden words is the important thing. It is the externalization of feeling in words and their release from the inner recesses of the mind, where they may have been causing tension, that we are after.

What at times seems to be homesickness may in reality turn

out to be something quite different. Not every boy or girl who fails to adjust happily to a camp or boarding school is just homesick. It was important to recognize this difference when things didn't go well with Ann during her first week at camp. Perhaps she was a little glum and disinterested on opening day, but in any event she attracted no special attention. On the third day she reported to the camp nurse complaining of diarrhea. She was put to bed, and although various treatments were tried nothing helped her, so she was sent to a metropolitan hospital for diagnostic studies and advice. Exhaustive tests there failed to uncover the cause of her ailment. By this time the fact that no other girl at camp had a similar ailment and the discrepancy between Ann's healthy appearance and the persistence of her symptoms made her physician suspect that her disorder had an emotional basis. He was right.

An unhurried talk with her disclosed a disturbance which X-rays and laboratory tests could never reveal. Ever since she could remember Ann had either been ignored or treated as though she were a nuisance by her parents. She had never been allowed to interfere with their trips, their pleasures, their business, or their social life. Camp had been the last straw. She hadn't been asked if she wanted to go to camp. She hadn't had any choice as to which camp. She hadn't been told anything except that she was to go, and on the day she was to leave home a neighbor took her to the train; her mother had 'an important engagement.' Rejected, unhappy, insecure, and full of resentment, Ann had at last expressed her long-repressed feelings by means of this symptom, diarrhea.

Ed, too, suffered more from rejection and suppressed hate than from plain homesickness. Ever since he was eight he had been sent off to camp and school. Now, in a new school, he withdrew from his activities, ignored his studies, and paid little attention to his companions' invitations to join them. Finally he almost burned to death in bed.

It should have been obvious that he was not just homesick.

In the first place he had been away from home many, many times before, and secondly he did not look wistful or depressed. What he wanted was recognition of his needs. He was determined to get attention and to get a chance to stay home *'if it kills me.'* Incredible as it may seem, his father couldn't understand why the boy should have deliberately climbed into bed and set fire to his mattress; but at least when pressed to do so, the father reluctantly consented to the boy's spending a year at home.

Homesickness will often be managed by the boy or girl himself. Only occasionally it will be as severe as Bill's or Lucy's. Rarely will it be confused with another type of trouble such as Ann's or Ed's. Commonly homesickness will be helped by such happenings as the acclaim which follows an unusually good dive, a lucky one-hand catch, or a fine drive, and such simple devices as being given a special responsibility or a prominent job. We have discussed the deeper type of homesickness because it clarifies by its exaggeration all homesickness, and once its real nature is known, it should be possible to handle the mild forms very efficiently. These are insecure, dependent young people. They need to feel accepted, they need support from others.

The kind of talking with these young people which has been discussed at some length in this chapter obviously can be applied to many other situations. Like conversation, it is an art; and only experience in using it will produce effective results. The teacher, counselor, club leader, or physician first using it will make mistakes, but when he has gained the satisfaction of seeing an upset adolescent develop poise and a new-found maturity as a result of such talks, this will far outbalance his earlier disappointments.

It is of the greatest importance, however, that anyone using this technique be constantly alert to its dangers to himself. The feeling of power that comes to one when this interviewing technique is successful can be very seductive and blind us to the vanity that is growing within us. We may become cock-sure, dogmatic, and overbearing, only to discover that the erst-while adolescent shuns us. Or we may become too daring and too convinced of our ability to carry on when only a psychia-trist should, only to discover that we have a youth with a seri-ous breakdown on our hands. Serious mental illness, brain tumors, and other organic diseases often appear first as rela-tively mild emotional upsets; many emotional upsets require much more skillful interviewing than the lay person can hope to have. Here is where the physician and the psychiatrist are needed. In such instances others' task is only to see that pro-fessional help is made available. Your purpose is to recognize the boy's or girl's trouble and to help: that someone who has professional training and experience may subsequently have to lend his aid in no way diminishes your contribution.

IX

Pitfalls of Testing

In order to study young people's needs, determine their aptitudes, estimate their progress, and investigate the reasons for their scholastic failure or predict their success, a variety of tests have been devised. These are *aids* to understanding — they do not give the complete answers. Based upon careful research and long experience, many of these tests can be of great help when they are properly interpreted, seen in proper perspective, and evaluated as one part of the entire picture. Too often tests are prematurely given undeserved weight.

A review of some of the possible factors in scholastic failure will clearly demonstrate this point. Facts concerning vision, hearing, growth, neurological and endocrine status, general health, cultural background, relationship to parents and siblings will obviously be pertinent items; and tests of intelligence, reading efficiency, skill in arithmetic and spelling, aptitudes, personality, and emotional status will be helpful. But to seize upon a single fact, such as poor vision, lack of siblings, rapid growth, low intelligence, slow reading, emotional instability, or a poor relationship with one parent as the cause of failure in school is to court serious error. A careful search for other causes and a thorough evaluation of the meaning and relevance of the item or test, as well as a thoughtful consideration of the adolescent as a whole, are necessary. To collect a fact, or to give a test and to score it, is not enough. There is a *person* involved, and thought must be given to the boy or girl and to how the fact or test result relates to him or to her. Many an adolescent who has poor vision, or who has had frequent illnesses, or who is a poor reader, or is excessively attached to his mother, or who has 'grown too fast' does well in school; too many who have good hearing, or are confident and who have grown in a more usual fashion, do poorly.

A single item or test may mean very little. How far astray one may be led by a single test is no better illustrated than by the tale, perhaps apocryphal, of the college applicant who was accepted chiefly because of his incredibly high score on a 'tweezer dexterity' test. His extraordinary degree of this aptitude had little relevance to his fitness for a college career, and this became evident when his propensity for stealing was found to exceed his interest in things academic! Not apocryphal, and really pathetic, is the story of the young boy whose annoying misbehavior in school was blamed on the fact that he was an 'only child' and therefore, by implication, 'spoiled' and 'needed discipline.' More thoughtful study revealed that his bad behavior stemmed from his worry over his failure to grow and mature as rapidly as his friends.

No single item, no single test, whether it be a simple one such as impaired vision or a more complex one such as projective test results should be swallowed whole. Take it into consideration, but don't be taken in by it. Look at the whole picture: don't accept a test result or a fact as the whole or the irrefutable answer. Parents are apt to choose, or to insist upon, a physical explanation for any problem, scholastic, behavioral, or emotional. Their stubborn avoidance of a psychological explanation often appears as unwarranted faith in the powers of hemoglobin, thyroxin, and fatigue: it is too often only wishful thinking, and sometimes a fear that their past mistakes will be revealed.

In order not to overlook any matter which may contribute to an adolescent's inefficient performance in school it is well to use a check list. Many factors other than the primary cause can be important and worth correcting. Vision should be at least briefly tested. A method such as the Massachusetts Vision Test, which, in addition to testing visual acuity at twenty feet, evaluates farsightedness and eye-muscle balance and gives consideration to symptoms of eye strain, should be used. To look for nearsightedness alone is not enough; farsightedness can also be disturbing. Faulty vision can and does cause eye strain and fatigue may well be a factor in poor scholastic perform- ance: at times it may be the only reason, but it is well to keep in mind the fact that a young person who is eager for an education will not let poor vision stand in the way.

Hearing, too, should be tested. Such simple methods as those which require only a watch, a whisper, or the gentle rubbing of the examiner's index finger and thumb can be used, and then supplemented, if there is any reason to suspect trouble, by tests with special instruments. It is well, too, to have a few sentences written from dictation. This may give an early hint of a difficulty in aural word recognition and will offer a sample of handwriting and spelling which may furnish helpful information. A handicap such as moderate deafness may not seem in itself to be a great barrier to learning, but because it makes early schooling difficult and unrewarding, it can color the child's attitude toward school and dampen his ardor. Severe deafness, early recognized and for which allowance has been made, is less damaging than an undetected moderate deafness, which compounds itself with frustration, loss of confidence, and a compensatory apparent lack of interest.

A boy's or girl's lassitude and indifference, born of disinterest in school, is too often thought to be evidence of anemia. Anemia is rarely present to a significant degree in a young person who is apparently in good health. Unfortunately, unless carefully done, a hemoglobin estimation may yield a low result and a parent's wishful thinking will be supported by an erroneous report. A 'low hemoglobin' as the cause of scholastic failure should always be regarded with great suspicion when the adolescent looks healthy, eats well, has had no recent severe illness and is energetic at everything but studies. However, to omit a hemoglobin test — as a matter of fact, to omit any part of a complete medical examination — is unwise, for when an opinion regarding the causes of failure in school is sought, a great deal is at stake. Though tests of vision and hearing or a medical examination may seem at times unrewarding and unnecessary, the occasional condition which they will reveal, and the reassurance which they offer, make them more than justified.

Thyroid deficiency is another undeservedly popular explanation of scholastic failure. When there is a true thyroid deficiency, an individual's processes are slowed down and as a result he may do poorly in school. However, this condition is uncommon. During early adolescence many children go through a period of being overweight; this is usually a perfectly normal part of their growth pattern. Given time, their glandular systems, now in an uneven state, will work themselves out in a satisfactory way. It is not wise to jump to the conclusion that the boy or girl who is overweight or indifferent or doing poorly in school needs thyroid. The implication that they are not normal, the support given to their development of the pill habit, and the interference with their own glands' peculiar but normal way of behavior all can do harm. If a boy is slow-acting and overweight (like his father!) for a while, or a girl's overweight is strongly reminiscent of her mother, it may disconcert the parents, but it is better to let adolescents grow and behave and develop in their own way than to attempt artificial means of modifying them. This does not mean that excessive weight is to be ignored. When there is a true glandular disorder, or an accompanying emotional disturbance, those should of course have the proper treatment.

Rate of growth and rate of maturation have effects on schoolwork which are more difficult to interpret than the matters already discussed. 'He is growing so fast' is a common excuse, but is it a valid one? Many boys who grow rapidly do well in school; and many who grow slowly do poorly. Many who grow rapidly have more interest in athletics and mechanics than they do in history and Latin, and the probability is that their scholastic failure may be due to something more subtle than their sudden increase in height. The extra energy they expended in growing was probably adequately balanced by the increased food intake. Rapid growth should, however, be noted: in the absence of other possible causes of failure, it, or at least concomitant emotional changes, may need consideration.

Marked variation in rate of physical maturation is a more likely cause of difficulty than most of the other physical factors because it is more deeply tinged with psychological implications. The desire to be large and masculine and the fear that he may not become so can upset a boy's behavior and performance. To remain flat-chested while her friends round out can disturb a girl who is trying hard to think and act in a more feminine fashion. The girl who persists in her interest in boys' games and shows no interest in dances or party dresses is more upset by her failure to develop than anything except her occasional excessive irritability would lead one to suspect. A boy who at fifteen is short and shows little evidence of advancing toward sexual maturity may become retiring, seem preoccupied, and fall off badly in his studies. Teasing in the shower-room and the handicap of his size at athletics add fuel to the flames. His failure to understand that wide variations in rate of maturing occur in perfectly normal boys makes the matter seem more serious than it need be. Retarded maturation, because of the anxiety it causes, is definitely to be kept in mind as a factor in scholastic failure.

To become sexually mature and to achieve full growth at an early age can also be a handicap, but hardly as troublesome a one as is slow development. Reliability and leadership rarely develop concomitantly with physical growth. The boy or girl who has the appearance of an adult seldom behaves like one and often suffers by failing to live up to his elders' expectations.

Matters such as not enough sleep, too many hours spent on a job or in extracurricular activities, or frequent or prolonged illness can so obviously detract from scholastic performance that it may seem trite to mention them, but in these days of our absorption in esoteric explanations of human behavior, the simple and obvious are sometimes forgotten. Joe may have scored poorly on a reading test, or Ed's projective test may have shown him to be confused by sex, but that Joe is working after school and up until ten at night in his father's store and that Ed is a member of practically every club and organization in school may be much more likely explanations of their poor marks.

Easy fatiguability too may be a factor but it is well to remember that interest is an important determinant of the amount of energy one exhibits. A severe illness or such an ailment as mononucleosis may lower vulnerability to fatigue, but young people recover quickly, and where lassitude persists, a lack of interest should be suspected. A boy or girl who seems perennially tired in school is often alert enough on the athletic field, at dramatics or over a dance week end: to blame late hours for their schoolroom fatigue is not only to make an error but also to miss an opportunity to help them to analyze their difficulty.

Their social setting and their position among their siblings are also important factors. It is reasonable to expect children born of parents of good educational background and cultural interests to have a considerable interest in things academic. Parents without these advantages often wish their children to have them: many of these young people may be little interested in a way of life differing from their parents'. This is not to say that some adolescents will not show an interest in ways not found in their homes, for obviously many of them do; but the lack of interest which some show can be better understood if one pays attention to their family culture. Allowance of course must be made for the fact that many adults who are cultured have had little schooling: they furnish a better environment for the development of their children's interest in things academic than will some who have had the opportunity of higher education but who have passed through it untouched. Adolescents' companions, too, modify their interests. They want to be like others. When their friends have little interest in school and no respect for cultural things, there is less likelihood that any one of them will enter wholeheartedly into these pursuits. Efforts by adults to give more applause to those who choose to, or dare to, exert themselves in their studies will help to combat this situation. It is heartening when adults, who often modify school schedules and school attendance to fit the needs of athletic contests, also make adjustments so that cultural opportunities or academic prize-giving can supplant a classroom exercise. Adolescents seek and need praise. They are more likely to seek scholastic honors when these honors are pointedly recognized and rewarded.

The 'only child' is traditionally a 'spoiled' one and by implication irresponsible and likely to do poorly in school. This is far from the case: adolescents who have many brothers and sisters also fail. It is the kind of person he or she is, and the way in which that adolescent was brought up which are the important factors. This fact is mentioned only because 'What would you expect; he's an only child' is so often heard that it has gained from repetition what it lacks in evidence. There is little reason to doubt that the boy's heredity, upbringing, emotional health, and factors in his environment are of much greater significance. The only child may have had more careful training and more opportunities, or he may have been treated in a possessive and indulgent fashion. The family constellation and setting are items to consider, but again not ones to pounce upon as the easy answer to a problem.

Medical findings and social facts do not furnish all the pitfalls to be avoided in the determination of the cause of a boy's failure in school. Psychological tests, so widely used today, are also open to misinterpretation. Their results should never be accepted without careful consideration. These tests furnish evidence, not answers: they are aids, not complete solutions.

Tests designed to measure achievement levels in reading, spelling, arithmetic, vocabulary, or grammar are valuable in estimating grade placement and relative abilities. Their administration increases the possibility of unreliability. There is a tendency to fail to scrutinize the tests for sources of error and for information other than the total scores. Low scores on a part or on all parts of such a test may be valid; but if there is reason to doubt it, or if a decision of considerable moment is involved, the test should be repeated. Fatigue on the day of the test, a lack of interest in the test, a deliberate or unconscious lack of effort from fear of failure or in order to 'save face,' or a simple misunderstanding of the test directions can effect the score.

Even a spelling test can lead one astray. Nowadays some spelling tests are designed in a 'multiple choice' manner. This allows machine scoring, but it eliminates the opportunity to observe quality of handwriting and — more important — that opportunity to see how the boy or girl would go about spelling the word. A spelling test which demands only that one of three or four spellings be selected as the correct one leaves much to be desired, and may yield a deceptively high score. Whenever anyone else gives you a spelling rating based on an achievement test, be sure to ask if it was obtained in this multiple-choice fashion. If so, repeat it, having the words written out by the boy or girl after they have heard you use them in a sentence.

Much of the value of group tests is lost if the scores of each subtest and their relation to each other is not studied. To know that a total score on an achievement test is 105 is much less helpful than to note that the reading was twice as good as the arithmetic, or to observe that it was the poor performance on the vocabulary and reading sections which lowered the total score, or to see in the many and bizarre spelling errors the hint of a language disability. It is also helpful to know whether a low score is due to many errors or to the fact that only a small number of questions were attempted: the former in- dicates the rapid but inaccurate work of a poorly informed or disinterested student and the latter of one who works slowly but accurately and who may be more capable than his score would indicate. Speed is a considerable factor in these tests, and under such a condition the potential ability of the slow, accurate worker can be underestimated.

Some of these achievement test scores may be converted

into intelligence quotients and this too can cause grave misinterpretation. Under most circumstances the IQ is regarded with too much awe. When it is derived from tests whose performance depends so greatly upon schooling as do achievement tests, it should be taken with a grain of salt. The IQ derived from an achievement test is greatly affected by reading ability, yet a poor reader may be very intelligent. In such an instance the test score is clearly reflecting reading ability, not intelligence. It is also affected by one's performance in mathematics and by knowledge of general information so the score may depend more upon the amount of schooling or background than upon native intelligence: a highly intelligent 'backwoods' boy or girl might score very poorly. It is also well to remember that these tests are at times given to groups under distracting conditions which may promote anxiety and thus affect the score.

In summary, use achievement tests but pay attention to more than the total score. Whenever there is reason to suspect the validity of a test result, do not hesitate to do so. It is better to repeat a test or to check its results against another than to put too much faith in what is, after all, an attempt to measure a very elusive and complicated attribute with a far from perfect instrument. These tests are best regarded as good screening devices. Their results are to be regarded like the news in the *Lisbon Falls Enterprise:* 'It may be so, it may not be so, but it *could be.*'

Individually administered intelligence tests, when carefully given, provide the most valid information regarding level of intelligence; but their expense is so much greater than the group achievement tests that it is impractical to use them widely or routinely. Up to age thirteen the Binet or the WISC is used and for older students the Wechsler-Bellevue. These tests are especially useful in the evaluation of those who have a language disability: since they do not require reading, this source of error is eliminated from the estimation of the intelligence.

However, despite their relatively greater expense and their requirement of greater skill in administration, these individual intelligence tests are far from foolproof. They measure extraordinarily well *what they are designed* to measure, but other factors than intelligence enter into scholastic performance. To say, for instance, that a boy is or is not college material on the basis of his Wechsler-Bellevue IQ can lead to serious error because it measures only one of the factors which determine scholastic success. The test does not measure drive, interest, emotional stability, aggressiveness, or passivity. We need, too, to remember that the boy's or girl's emotional state may considerably affect the intelligence rating. One should always look at the note describing the test — not just the 'score.' A nervous, apprehensive student may do very poorly on a test; we have to be sure that we are not getting an index of anxiety rather than an estimate of intellectual capacity. These are limitations rather than faults of the test: the fault is with those who assign it powers it does not have. The intelligence test is an aid to forming opinions, but its result needs interpretation and understanding, not blind acceptance. Carl's story illustrates this point.

Enuresis (bedwetting) which had persisted up to his fifteenth year brought Carl to our attention. In his second year at boarding school he appeared to be a reliable, plodding, unimaginative sort and his school grades were just above passing. He resisted any suggestion that he might do better were he to drop one course and concentrate on the others, but he was clearly under continual tension lest he fail and there seemed little likelihood of conquering his enuresis while this situation persisted. When the result of his first Wechsler-Bellevue Intelligence Test was ready, it was difficult to accept its accuracy: all the subtest scores were low and the IQ, a figure usually considered incompatible with college preparatory work. Later the test was repeated by another competent examiner and an equally low score was obtained.

Throughout his early secondary school years Carl resisted every effort to lighten his load, but eventually he acquiesced and reluctantly lengthened his college preparatory course by an extra year. At first he apparently feared that to accept any help might indicate his unfitness for college work; to go through college was his all-absorbing purpose — that he would do, no matter what. But gradually, as he felt this purpose of his was understood, he talked more, was less suspicious of proffered help, and lost some of his tension; but only his extraordinary drive toward this one goal can explain his success. His marks were never good, but he 'passed,' he 'graduated,' and he was admitted to a good college. Not to have recognized this drive, and to have accepted his low IQ as irrefutable evidence of his inability ever to go to college, would have been to make a tragic error.

Too frequently we meet a boy or girl who is in strong contrast to Carl. Sandra was such a one. The youngest daughter of a wealthy family of long and respected tradition in their town, she had been sent to boarding school, where she did fairly well in her studies with little effort. On the basis of her intelligence (her Wechsler-Bellevue IQ was 135) she was accepted by a top-rank college despite the fact that her marks were little more than passing. After two months in college she resigned: she found it 'dull' and 'too difficult.' Next she tried a small college which her family thought would be 'more sympathetic,' but after a few months she was dropped out because of low grades. Her intelligence was just as high as her tests indicated, but those tests were of little value in predicting her success in college. Sandra's obvious passivity, aimlessness, and irresponsibility were factors which outweighed her intelligence.

Cultural background and school have to be taken into consideration in evaluating the results of even the individual type of intelligence test. The test is heavily weighted with vocabulary and information, items which put a backwoods or foreign boy or girl of good intelligence at a considerable disadvantage. How many who glibly quote IQs are familiar with the items upon which the score is based? A look at the component parts of some of the Wechsler-Bellevue subtests will quickly make obvious how an intelligent but untutored boy or girl might obtain a low score.

The error of trying to make distinctions or predictions based upon narrow differences in IQ is a common one, particularly in institutions which have high admission standards. The differences in IQ may actually be valid, but so many other factors enter into scholastic performance that to make a judgment upon the small differences in IQ which exists in highly selected groups is to place a poor bet. Students admitted to a high-grade college vary more in academic performance than they do in intelligence: a group of those who attain good grades may be found to have about the same average intelligence quotient as do those who have low grades. Within the narrow and high range of IQ one finds in such a school or college, emotional stability and motivation have more to do with quality of performance than the small differences in intelligence rating. This is illustrated by a recent study of a group of honor students and a like number who stood at the bottom of their college class. These two groups had an average difference in intelligence level of only about five points. However, when the emotional health of the two groups was compared, a striking difference was found. The honor students showed a far healthier emotional adjustment than those whose academic performance was poor.

The individually administered intelligence test is a valuable aid in the diagnosis of scholastic failure, but neither its expense nor its need for technical skill in administration should lend it immunity to critical analysis or clothe it with omniscience. Use it, but recognize its limitations and don't expect it to furnish information beyond its scope.

New techniques, perhaps because they are unfamiliar and little understood, are often accepted unquestioningly. Projective tests have recently fallen heir to this doubtful privilege. Immensely helpful as a research tool, often very helpful in clinical practice, they are hardly well enough developed or authenticated for adolescents to be of general use and are certainly unfit for other than expert interpretation. Nonetheless the addition of techniques which reveal some of the unconscious factors in an adolescent's behavior are welcome additions to the psychometrist's armamentarium. Their value should be recognized if for no other reason than that they emphasize the importance of the emotions in scholastic achievement. Properly used and cautiously interpreted, they can be a real help in understanding the adolescent whose failure in school is baffling.

The Rorschach, the Thematic Apperception Test and varieties of the Sentence Completion Test are the projective techniques most commonly employed. It may be true that these tests reveal little that a psychiatric interview would not uncover, but their ability to disclose probable sources of conflict and to set goals for psychotherapy is well recognized when the tests are administered by a psychologist with good clinical experience. One has to keep in mind, however, that most of these techniques are very time-consuming and therefore very expensive. The relatively short time required for their administration is deceptive: it may take little longer than an hour to administer a Rorschach or TAT but it will require several hours to score and interpret it.

Projective tests too have their pitfalls. A projective test may suggest that there is a severe emotional disorder, but this evidence should be supported by other signs and data. The primary difficulty may in reality be due to a lack of intelligence commensurate with the level of studies being attempted, or a preference and aptitude for things mechanical rather than academic, rather than the deep-seated conflicts the projective test reveals. It is surprising, too, how well some boys do their schoolwork while under severe emotional stress, though no doubt these boys would do even better were these conflicts removed.

Not only will a rare boy do well in spite of his emotional handicap, but also it is important to remember that a boy's emotional disturbances may not be as grave as his projective test would seem to imply. This is not a fault of the test: it derives from a failure to remember when interpreting the test that adolescents are in a period of transition, that they are *normally* confused, and consequently they may give test responses which would properly cause grave concern if obtained from an adult. The adolescent who 'overidentifies' with his mother, according to a projective test today, may change considerably within a few weeks. Boys whose tests give evidence of severe emotional disturbances may be well and happy in a few months, rather than in the throes of schizophrenia. Adolescents are in a state of flux — their emotions swing wide and violently before setting into adult balance, and this transition factor must be taken into account when projective test responses are interpreted.

In conclusion, it must be kept constantly in mind that any tool is only as effective as the workman who uses it. Clinical experience, preferably comparable to the extensive amount required of the psychiatrist, is a prime desideratum in assaying the validity of psychological tests. In the hands of the amateur they, like any other instrument, may be both dangerous and ineffective.

It is not necessary to test and re-test and to examine and re-examine, but it is important not to jump at conclusions and to avoid clichés. It is imperative to devote time to studying the tests, the facts *and the individual*. Test results are both too blindly accepted and too often deprecated; it is important to know their uses as well as their abuses, their value as well as their limitations. The hemoglobinometer, the Wechsler-Bellevue, the audiometer and the Rorschach are all helpful instruments, but they can't do the thinking necessary if one is to reach a wise decision as to the cause of a boy's scholastic failure. When a person — and a person who is in a period of growth and transition — is involved, his whole picture, not just a single fact, must be given consideration if error is to be avoided.

X

Scholastic Failure

Schooling is important to adolescents and frequently a source of considerable anxiety to them. After all, school is their *business*, just as is a man's job or career his business. How they succeed at it, what goes on during the school day, what it yields them in the way of mastery and defeat, acceptance and rejection, pleasure and pain — are all very significant. School is an important part of the medical history of any adolescent: it is a subject which no one who deals with the physical or emotional problems of adolescence can ignore.

Determination of the cause or causes of scholastic failure requires careful thinking. Laziness and indifference are rarely the cause of failure. Some adolescents are by nature, aptitude, or interest unsuited for some types of schooling; but many who do poorly can, once the real reason for their failure is known, do well in their former, or in a different, field of study. The first step in helping them is a painstaking search for the cause of failure: this is a process which demands careful thought and an avoidance of hasty conclusions and popular clichés. The importance of knowing the boy as well as simply his test scores and a few facts has been discussed in the preceding chapter.

Facts and tests one may have, and in order to avoid omitting a significant point it is well to have a check list; but be ready to depart from this list whenever it seems likely that information will be gathered more satisfactorily in some other order. If a boy or girl wants to talk, by all means let him: tomorrow he may not feel like telling you the really important thing. You always learn much more by listening than from the best or from the newest 'test' which you had planned to give.

Before considering in detail some of the more common causes of scholastic failure, it may be well to make some comment about the sort of result one can expect from a study of an adolescent who is doing poorly in school. If the result of your effort is considered successful only in those instances where subsequently there is a complete reversal in scholastic performance, your successes may be few. But if to have helped to change a maladjusted adolescent into a well-adjusted and effective one is considered a successful result, even though there may have been need to change schools, grade, or subjects, the percentage improved will be much higher. It seems clear that the improvement of the adjustment to life or to the educational process should be the aim.

Some apparently difficult educational problems arise from the fact that a parent, or the customs of the boys' or girls' group, has placed them in an educational setting to which they are unsuited. This does not mean that they are uneducable; it only means that a square peg has failed to fit into a round hole. If a transfer into another 'easier' type of education has to be made, this may seem to some to constitute an unsuccessful result; but impartial observers will not agree. Education is a broad term: it covers more than one school or one course or even more than schools themselves have to offer. What the neighborhood school and its courses offer is the most general and convenient means of education; that these may be unsuited to an occasional adolescent is inevitable. At times the best way to solve a boy's or girl's schooling problem is temporarily to take him out of it. A job or apprentice learning can mature some for whom formal schooling seems only to perpetuate immaturity.

To find just the right setting or remedy for the adolescent who is failing in school is the aim of investigations such as will be described. Often neither the school, the grade, nor the subjects will need to be changed; but when a good adjustment is unlikely within them, it is sensible to admit it and to suggest a change. Change for its own sake is never justifiable — usually that is no more than an admission of defeat or evidence of exhausted patience.

Intelligence is an obvious factor to be investigated in any study of the cause of scholastic failure. Its level is of most importance when a boy or girl is attempting a course for which a superior intelligence is essential: failure in a course of study which does not demand high intelligence is most likely due to some other cause. To label a student stupid just because of failure is thoughtless. There may not be a sufficiently high level of intelligence to permit successful handling of a difficult subject, but the same student may perform well, perhaps even brilliantly, in another type of course. It is better to say that such a one does not seem suited for, or capable of, the present course rather than to call a boy or girl stupid. Stupidity implies hopelessness. Many who have done very poorly in a college preparatory curriculum have done exceedingly well in a business course or in mechanics or art. Some who have been called stupid have later turned in excellent performances in subjects which formerly seemed beyond their grasp. Not a few of them make a better adjustment and contribution in adult life than do their more successful schoolmates.

Not only should level of intelligence be thought of in terms of the type of studies the student is attempting, but also one's opinion of the extent of its influence should be affected by the character of the student's interest and drive. As we have said, one whose intelligence is at the lower limits of that which is compatible with college work, but whose interest in going to college is great, may well do better in college than indifferent and purposeless students of high intelligence.

Inferior intelligence, however, can be the primary cause of failure. It is important to recognize this and to adjust the educational program so that self-respect and confidence can be maintained and an opportunity given for a type of training which will fit the boy or girl for a useful life. There are courses in schools for boys and girls whose level of intelligence is too low for college preparatory work, and there are many simple virtues and useful skills which can be developed in the place of a knowledge of Latin or chemistry.

Such simple matters as improper grade placement and a lack of knowledge of fundamentals should not be forgotten in a search for the cause of failure. Through illness, a family's move from one town to another, or parents' insistence that a boy hurry through school, a boy may be found to be in a grade too advanced for him. Almost always such a situation will be straightened out by the school, but it should be kept in mind. More commonly found is the effect of a poor knowledge of fundamentals. Not infrequently a pupil, through lack of interest, poor teaching, or a poor relationship with a teacher in one grade, or through illness, will miss some fundamental points or training but will push along to higher levels where this lack is a serious handicap. Embarrassed to ask what others may think a silly or stupid question, or perhaps restrained from showing an interest in things academic by their companions' indifference to them, confused and failing, they will plod on and seek satisfaction from extracurricular activities. These are the ones who benefit from tutoring, or, in some cases, from a change in schools. Often 'face saving' will block any improvement until some such step is taken. They find it difficult to ask a question about a sixth-grade matter in front of their quick-to-laugh eighth-grade companions.

At the present time one factor frequently blamed for failure in school is 'slow reading.' Out of this have grown such comments as that reading is poorly taught nowadays; that movies, radio, and television are making children illiterate; and that all this trouble could be averted if the present-day 'flash card' method of teaching reading were abandoned and the old-fashioned phonetic method re-instated. Undoubtedly there is some truth in all of this. Certainly no one method of teaching anything can be the best for everyone. But talk about the good old days should be taken with a grain of salt. Despite the alleged poor teaching, movies, radio, and television nowadays there are many children who read very well, and many who read more efficiently and more widely than their elders. The fact essential to remember is that inefficient reading can be a very real handicap and should be looked for whenever scholastic failure occurs. Boys and girls who read slowly, who plod through books and homework at a rate both painful and frustrating, soon begin to believe that they dislike reading and do as little of it as possible. By avoiding practice in reading they then become more and more inept at it, and fall even farther behind their classmates.

A few points should be kept in mind. In the first place all children are not able to read at the same rate. Just because a boy or girl reads more slowly than the average of the class means neither that this is the cause of failure nor that reading should be 'speeded up.' They may be reading at a rate which is proper for a person of their intelligence. Before any decision is reached, this and other factors must be taken into consideration. Nothing is gained by attempting to make a slow thinker read too rapidly. Many, to be sure, who read slowly can be taught to read more rapidly and will at the same time improve their comprehension; but when one is attempting to help a student who is failing badly, it is essential to remember that rate of reading and degree of intelligence have some relationship. Remember, too, that some people just plain do things slowly. They like it that way. Unfortunately their slow pace may annoy their parents and teachers. Nevertheless, there is nothing inherently perfect about the hell-bent-for-election pace of modern living, and it is well now and then to stop to realize that these few more deliberate people may be just as 'right' as we are. At any rate anything more than an initial attempt or two at speeding them up will probably do no more than increase their resentment, make them more stubborn, and increase their passive resistance to your more hectic way of living.

Poor reading may be a sign of a specific language disability. It may be just one bit of evidence that the pupil's failure is due to a lack of facility in handling words in any one of a number of other ways — speaking, writing, or spelling — and the failure not caused by poor reading alone. The treatment which such a boy or girl will need is very different from that which will help a student whose poor reading is caused by long absence from school, lack of interest, poor teaching, or an emotional upset; and these must not be confused with one another. Specific language disability and its management will be discussed in detail later in this chapter.

Finally, a word of caution about the inevitability of scholastic failure when there is poor reading. It is a handicap, but some will surmount it and do exceedingly well in spite of it.

Like any of the other possible causes of failure, it may not be the sole or the most important factor: it causes disaster more readily in some personalities than in others. This fact points to the desirability of looking for poor reading skill in those who do quite well. They, too, can be worthy of some special help and attention!

A specific language disability of sufficient degree to constitute a significant handicap is thought to occur in about 10 per cent of males and in a much smaller proportion of females. This difference in incidence in the sexes and its tendency to develop in varying forms in many members of some families have suggested that it has a genetic basis. No one theory concerning its cause is widely accepted. On the one hand, those who believe its basis to be primarily genetic have developed a number of methods of treatment of varying degrees of effectiveness, of which Orton's is perhaps as widely used as any. On the other hand increasing acceptance is being given to emotional origins of reading disability. Language therapists stress the importance of the emotional tone established between patient and therapist and the value of interview techniques in facilitating emotional release with a concomitant improvement in reading ability.

Reading has also been found to be closely related to attitudes toward the taking in of food and toward all the bodily activities concerned with taking in and giving out. In his book *Psychoanalysis and the Education of the Child*, Pearson cites an impressive number of cases in which both scholastic failure and reading disability have been corrected as a result of intensive psychotherapy. Perhaps some of the exercises of the organicists combined with the emotional catharsis of the school of depth psychology will eventually prove to be the most effective treatment approach for some.

The boy or girl who is handicapped by a hitherto unrecognized specific language disability is typically one who was late in learning to talk, had difficulty in learning to read, is not a glib talker, found spelling difficult and arithmetic relatively easy to learn, and has more relatives who have a lack of facility in handling words than is found in the average family. When tested they may have very high intelligence, but will hesitate and mispronounce words as they read aloud, spell atrociously, score poorly on a reading test, and show evidence of uncertainty (evidenced by variation in the slant of letters, in pencil pressure, and in the spacing between letters, writing over, and erasures) in their handwriting. In school, their performance in mathematics and science may be excellent, but they will usually do poorly in foreign languages (though they will do much better in grammar than in vocabulary or in writing from dictation) and in courses requiring much reading and writing. Not many who have this difficulty will show all these signs or symptoms, but many will have several of them. A few will stutter or lisp, most will be unable to read aloud correctly and fluently, few will care for acting or debating, and few will have facility in remembering names or in talking extempore. Most will be very poor spellers. Not only will they fail a large proportion of the words on a spelling test, but they will make bizarre errors, reversing letters, confusing one sound for another, and omitting sounds. They will usually say that they can learn to spell a word but that this is relatively difficult for them and that they tend soon to forget it. Often, in order to avoid spelling errors, they use a limited written vocabulary, and when given their own choice of words, their difficulty may go unnoticed. For this reason the importance of giving a spelling test for which they have not studied as a screening device and diagnostic aid cannot be overemphasized. Some read quite well, but few as well as their intelligence would permit. Many have trouble with foreign languages because of their lack of aptitude in associating sounds and letters; unless there is some special reason for learning a foreign language, it is wise for them to concentrate upon improving their facility in handling their own.

The very considerable variation in degree of language disability which can exist makes it possible for it to go unnoticed for several years. A mild disability may apparently be no handicap to an intelligent child in the early years, but it will show up as a serious one when more advanced schooling puts a much greater demand upon his ability to use words. Sometimes a disability may not be noticed until the heavy reading, writing, and foreign-language demands and the higher standards of college work are encountered. This is not to say that the disability did not always exist or did not previously act as a hindrance to optimal scholastic performance. Often, however, a bright and ambitious boy or girl will not let a mild disability stand in the way of doing well in the lower grades but will find it frustrating and next to impossible to conquer when faced with more lengthy and more exacting studies.

The fact that a specific language disability may be mild, go unnoticed, and may *apparently* be little handicap to *some* children in the early grades is no excuse for not attempting its early diagnosis and treatment. Too often, when untreated, it fosters the development of feelings of frustration and leads to a child's dislike of school and learning and to the development of behavior disorders. When proper remedial help is given these children, their behavior problems disappear in time. Once they feel that someone has recognized their trouble and is doing something to help them, they are relieved. The improvement in their handling of words comes more slowly.

The matter of intelligence is very important in this connection. Judged on the basis of school performance, a boy or girl who has a specific language disability might be thought stupid, and were this same boy to be given an achievement test heavily laden with vocabulary, reading, and sometimes spelling, he may score very poorly. Such a student should be given an intelligence test which does not depend heavily upon language ability. Not all who have a specific language disability have high intelligence, but many who do will be found to have high IQs when a Stanford-Binet or Wechsler-Bellevue Intelligence Test is administered.

The remedial method based upon the Orton theory has been outlined in detail by Gillingham and Stillman. This method attempts to build and reinforce in one cerebral hemisphere the visual, auditory and kinesthetic associations between sounds and letters. Subsequently when these are heard or seen the proper corresponding cerebral image will be more readily and correctly recalled. This method employs repeated careful drill on the sound, look, and feel first of letters and later of syllables. There is daily careful drill on phonetics and on writing from dictation, and careful training in reading with an emphasis on orderly attention to words rather than speed. When this sort of drill is given individually, attention can be given to each child's particular needs, and the likelihood of his repeatedly drilling in an erroneous fashion is obviated.

Such retraining can be tedious and dull, but in the hands of an enthusiastic, imaginative, and well-trained teacher few children fail to be considerably benefited and to be appreciative of its help. The object is to establish vivid association patterns for the sound, look, and feel of letters — and that takes time.

The importance of a sustained and repeated contact with an enthusiastic adult whose whole attention and interest is devoted to the student during the remedial session has an emotional value of great worth. After all it cannot fail to impress most young people when an intelligent adult painstakingly devotes his or her entire attention to a matter which has frustrated and penalized them. In fact, it may very well be the devotion of the therapist and the affectionate response in the child that furnishes a good part of the motivation for overcoming the language disability.

Often, too, there are new handwriting habits to establish. The boy or girl may be left-handed and may have learned to write in a clumsy upside-down fashion — though this disability is not more common among strongly left-handed than among right-handed individuals — instead of the proper left-handed position with the forearm parallel to the paper's slant. Or, being left-handed, the student may need a left-handed table-chair, or be allowed to pull up an adjacent chair, so that it will not be necessary to twist his body into an awkward position when writing. One student who came to us with the complaint of low back pain was completely relieved of it when given a chair fitted with a left-handed writing arm. When writing seated in a right-handed chair it had been necessary for him to twist his trunk into an unnatural position; and this, aided to a considerable extent by the tension which always accompanied his attempts to write because of his language disability, produced real discomfort.

Illness or prolonged absence from school may be the obvious cause of scholastic failure, and little need be said regarding them. The frequency with which they are blamed is, however, much greater than is justified, and the warnings mentioned in an earlier chapter are worth reiterating. Illness can be debilitating, but the degree to which it incapacitates and keeps a student from studying can be vastly affected by their elders' attitude toward it and by their own interest in things academic. Some, when ill, ask for their books and keep up with their classes; others, no more ill, settle back into a state of complete irresponsibility and rest their minds as well as their livers. Sickness — a bad fracture, anemia, or a low metabolic rate — may be a factor in failure, but these are more often than not excuses which mask such causes as lack of aptitude or an emotional disorder.

A few instances will arise in which it is difficult to tell whether illness or some other physical factor is really to blame for failure. When the cause is physical, there will be a time relationship between the cause and the failure, an absence of other periods of failure, and an evident desire to do better on the student's part. At this point it is well to mention the importance of adolescents' having their own physician and of their going to him by themselves. Their doctor may also be the family's doctor, but it is important that they have a physician to whom they can go and to whom they can give their own explanation of their problems. This explanation may later be supplemented by a parent who feels that some point has been left out or not emphasized sufficiently, but this is very different from a parent's telling the whole story while an annoyed youth sits by. Going to their own doctor by themselves increases their sense of maturity and gives them a feeling of responsibility for their problem. In addition, it gives the doctor the advantage of hearing the story in their own words colored by their own feelings. The saving in time and error which this may avoid is considerable.

Past illnesses as well as present health can be significant factors in scholastic failure. A mild cerebral palsy, either overlooked or concealed by unhappy parents, may explain a gradual decline in scholastic success. When the damage to the intellect is not great, it becomes a noticeable factor only when the demands put upon it by the more difficult work of the upper grades become greater. A severe meningitis may leave damage: that it is the cause of relatively poor performance can be suspected when good schoolwork antedated the illness.

Not all adolescents transplant easily. Wrenched from their old friends and old school by their families' move to a new town, some go through a long period of readjustment which is reflected in their poor performance in school. That the cause is really this, and not the daydreaming or sullenness which may be more obvious, will be suggested by a contrast in their previous and their present school records, and can be verified by inquiry into their acceptance by their present group. Poor adjustment to their group can also show up as a determining factor in those whose families have not moved, or in those who go off by themselves to boarding school or college. Adolescents vary in their need of acceptance by their group and in their ability to adapt to a new one, but all of them perform much better when their presence is at least noticed and when they receive occasional recognition and applause.

It is true that some boys who seem to have no friends and few companions do well in their studies. A few bury themselves in their books and excel. Unless they are unusually gifted, they too may be said to fail, for their way is not one which is a good preparation for effective living. Given opportunities for friendship, led into appropriate activities, they might improve their facility to establish interpersonal relationships and lead better adjusted lives.

Rebellion is often associated with scholastic failure. When an adolescent is thwarted in his effort to become independent he will fight this restraint with the few weapons he has at his disposal, even though they may not be ones he cares to use. The father who is going to make a doctor out of his son, no matter what the son wants, may find himself baffled by his intelligent son's atrocious marks; the father who denies the sense of a career in art and insists on a Yale education may find himself hunting for a son who has not only failed in school but also run away from home; the harsh, critical, demanding, and never-praising father may expect to have a son who will rebel against teachers and try to annoy and defeat them at every turn. To him they are just another symbol of authority.

There is usually much more pressure on boys than on girls to do well in school, but nowadays there are social pressures on girls too for scholastic accomplishment, and these, together with parents' ambitions, make success in school more pertinent to an adolescent girl's adjustment than was formerly the case. Most of the reasons for a boy's failure in school apply equally well to them, but in addition their performance may be affected by their confusion as to their role in life and by their conflicting emotions. They need to reconcile their sexual needs and their changing attitude toward boys with present-day demands for more education and more participation in community affairs. A choice must be made between mother-hood and a career, or a combination of both. These are new problems, toward whose solution parents and friends can offer little help from their own experience. Yet how adolescent girls meet them and how they readjust their childhood feelings toward boys and strive to accept the demands of adulthood will determine their future effectiveness and happiness.

Carol's failure in school was blamed on her 'irresponsibility' and 'daydreaming.' A healthy, highly intelligent, attractive sixteen-year-old, she was as mixed up as it would seem pos-sible to be. Not deeply unhappy, she vacillated between the most childish and the most mature comments and plans. She seemed alternately to be facing and then escaping or evading adulthood. In one breath boys were 'stuck up' and detestable; in the next she couldn't mention one's name without a deep blush. She adored her father and wanted to follow in his foot-steps, but she couldn't bear to have him even touch her. She 'loathed' school, and wanted to go to a medical school. Her girl friends were 'just silly' about boys, but she didn't want to be an old maid like her aunt. 'I wish I could get way out west.'

Carol's conversation, like her mind, was full of questions: 'Why do I feel this way? Why don't I like them any more? Should I go to college? Why does my mother nag me all the time? Do you think it's silly of me to want to go to camp? Why does my father make me feel funny?'

Carol's daydreaming was hardly profitless woolgathering, and her real concern for her feelings and future far from ir-responsibility. She needed time, encouragement, and an opportunity to discuss her feelings and questions — she needed insight, not nagging, not impatience.

Girls strive to be like their friends. This makes them fearful to be alone or to be different. At the same time a girl wants to be herself, to maintain her individuality. Some meet this problem by adopting an outer conformity; others ignore it, evade it, or postpone efforts to solve it. During these years girls are often mature and very realistic in one area and evasive and childish in another. This is to say that they are accepting responsibility at school and in clubs but remaining docile, obedient, and dependent at home. In this they are failing to move toward satisfactory family relationships.

A boy's relationship to, and attitude toward, adult males is a potent factor in his scholastic success. If his feeling toward his father is one of aggression and antagonism, if he no longer has any desire to please or emulate him, he may make little effort in his studies. When his relationship to his father is a good one, however, his attitude toward his teachers and his school is likely to be good. Usually a boy's antagonism toward his father will not be obvious. The boy may often not be aware of it himself, and over a period of years he may have come to accept their relationship as the usual state of affairs rather than as undesirable and unusual. Not having anyone to whom he can express these feelings, perhaps suppressing them and never facing them himself, they exert even more powerful influence on his behavior.

Ed's parents were generally regarded as fine citizens. Intelligent, able college graduates, they took an active part in many of their community's affairs. His father ran a large industrial plant very successfully, was frequently off on trips, usually worked late, and came home tired and was 'not to be disturbed': his week ends were devoted to travel or to golf, which 'kept up his business contacts.' When Ed was fourteen his father decided to send him to what he thought was a fine school 'which would teach him how to study.' It didn't, and he got into just as much trouble as he dared. The letters home about his misconduct infuriated his father, and did not disturb — in fact seemed to please — Ed. In his final year, now seventeen, he dared more and more, and was finally asked to leave.

Ed freely admitted that he had deliberately gone about having himself expelled. 'I told my father the school was no good and that I didn't want to stay there, but he's always right, he always has to have his own way, and anyway he's too busy to listen. This was the only way I could beat him. I've no respect for the school. They make rules but they don't dare enforce them. They finally had to!'

Drinking, out all night, breaking rules, he was rebelling against his father's domination and showing his disregard of a father and a school he didn't respect. The teachers were as fair game to beat as was his father. Never close to his father, never wanting to be like him, and having found no man at this school whom he would like to imitate, he floundered hopelessly when faced with the need to grow up and to become an effective man. Confused and dependent, he needed strong but warm and understanding support.

A busy father, successful and demanding of his adult associates, needs to give thought to the importance of finding time to interest himself in his son and to be generous in praising early efforts. Too often in an effort to cancel what seems to him a mother's too-easy praise, he makes himself appear heartless and without affection. What he would protest is only for the boy's own good may in reality widen the gulf between them. From that point on, it is less likely that the boy will ask his opinion or seek his praise; instead he may become increasingly attached to his mother, hardly a desirable state in his adolescent years.

Not infrequently a poor father-son relationship will apparently act as a strong motivating force; but it is important to realize that such a one is neither healthy nor efficient. The boy who does well to spite his father would undoubtedly do still better were he free of this feeling. He certainly would be a much more emotionally healthy individual without it. The embittered boy who, when asked what he is going to do after graduation blurts out that the first thing he is going to do is to stuff his diploma down his father's throat, may have studied hard to win that diploma but may be less well off than a boy who hasn't one; it can be better to have good feelings toward one's father than to have a diploma won only to spite him.

No better, either for the boy or for his studies, than a poor relationship with his father is an adolescent's too-close attachment to his mother. These are the passive, dependent, spiritless boys with little drive or purpose of their own. Pleasant, often charming, gentle and ineffective, they fail to utilize their capacities and profess no understanding of why they should do so. Dependent, they fear the failure that might come if they were to try their own wings. Lacking all semblance of aggression, they avoid the responsibilities and efforts which success would subsequently demand of them. Afraid to take on the demands of a man's role, they make a virtue of their apathy and deprecate others' show of reasonable ambition.

Anger over real or fancied unfairness or even cruelty does not always come out in word or action but may be repressed where, because of its power and need to be discharged, it will seek devious outlets. Such outlets are usually hidden or distorted and may seem to have no connection with their true source. Steve felt he had better leave school and go to work. As a freshman and sophomore he had made consistently high grades in all his subjects and he had taken part in many extra-curricular activities.

This boy's parents owned and ran a successful factory of special electrical devices, and with considerable pride he told of the struggles his parents had had in their early years. His mother was plainly the dynamo behind the enterprise, possessed boundless energy, and handled business matters most aggressively. As the boy talked more of the part played by his mother, he drew a picture of a powerful woman who ruled the entire family with a smothering authority. Despite the fact that he was now twenty years of age, he had only recently been allowed to drive the car at all and still never when his mother went along; she invariably took the wheel and drove with a reckless disregard for others.

Steve told of an episode in which he had decided to buy some clothes for the summer. After mentioning his intention at supper, no more had been said, but as he left the house to go in town to shop the following morning, his mother drove into the yard, having already gone into town and bought him a complete summer wardrobe. Though he now related this episode angrily, when it had occurred he had maintained his usual silence, so he was encouraged to talk about it and to recall and talk about similar episodes. Gradually more and more of his anger and resentment toward his mother came out, and as they did, over a period of several weeks, his attitude toward his studies slowly improved. Finally he began to see continuing in school as a means of avoiding the domination of his mother and as a place where he could prepare himself for the showdown with her as to who was going to run his life. At the Christmas vacation period there was a violent scene, but when his new-found independence became evident, his mother saw the great need her son had to assert himself and began to give him freedom to do so. Slowly the entire atmosphere of the home took on a completely different character. His father, after years of bowing to his aggressive wife's demands and maintaining a hands-off position with his son, began to set up a healthy father-son relationship. The following year this student graduated with high honors. He had become happy and effective, and his speech and manner showed his new-found maturity.

For many years this boy had rebelled against his mother's rule silently and subtly with great hostility, but most ineffectively and disastrously, not being at all aware of the way in which his rebellion was influencing his behavior. He had fought the dependency his mother imposed on him by every means at his disposal but the right one, namely, talking it out and getting to understand what caused his discontent and failure.

Every adult has within himself infantile and childish and adolescent ways of responding to life that he has never given up or left behind in their proper places in his life. These old unresolved habits of feeling and acting cause various types of emotional illness. Rex, though a college senior, was typical of many who are in their teens. After three very good college years, he was now failing in his work, unable to concentrate, wanted to leave school, and was completely discouraged. He had lived alone with his mother since the age of two, when his father had walked out on them never to be heard from again. Lacking a male to imitate and a father to help him in the normal breaking of his dependent and affectionate ties with his mother, he had continued to behave emotionally like a child of five or six. His ties to his mother were still intense at eighteen.

In contrast to his violent feeling of attachment to his mother, his attitude toward girls of his own age was marked by shyness, discomfiture in their company, and a constant state of revery about making love to them. Dreaming of being their hero had taken much time that Rex should have used for study. His fixation at a childhood level of feeling was so strong that he had transferred much of this emotion to his alma mater. The result was that he had a deep-seated dread of graduating from college and of going out into the competitive world of adult life. It soon became clear that to ward off this threat he had unconsciously tried to fail so that he could return to college for another year.

Depending upon a college as a mother substitute is not uncommon. Numbers of brilliant but emotionally immature, dependent people unconsciously avoid the aggressive and competitive world of adulthood by pursuing year after year an interminable program of advanced study. Hangers-on around a university at thirty-five years of age, they have little academic standing but are content to eke out a very modest livelihood in order that they may remain within the protection of its walls.

A close attachment to his mother is proper and healthy in a boy's early years and should continue as an affectionate relationship as he grows older; but as a boy develops he should become increasingly independent and show a more and more positive relationship toward adult males and their roles. He needs more confidence in himself and less support as he grows older, more opportunities to do things and to make decisions himself. Boys need not become aggressively selfish, but they need to be allowed to develop their own initiative and a chance to imitate effective males rather than to bask in the shelter and support of their own mothers, or later with such substitutes as Alma Mater.

Adolescent boys vary in native degree of maleness or masculinity, independence and aggressiveness, as in other characteristics. Some break from their mothers early and assume masculine roles and relationships when barely entering their teens. Others, despite their mothers' determined efforts to cut the apron strings, are slow to show initiative and to take on responsibility. There is no set age or state of development which is normal or average for this change from dependence to independence, from mother attachment to a positive relationship with adult males. There is only the need that this transition be recognized and abetted, not thwarted. It can be disastrous to throw a boy overboard and tell him to sink or swim, but it is equally unwise not to give him every chance to learn to strike out for himself. Some will need more help and patience than others; some will not be ready to try at as early an age as others; but all should be given the opportunity. Too much protection, too long continued, destroys their initiative and is poor preparation for their adult life.

Finally, remember that a poor student today, instead of being stupid and hopeless, may in reality be a 'slow starter.' Many a mediocre student has blossomed out into a real scholar in later years: patience with them and confidence in them can be more rewarding than a too-hasty and too-strong adverse opinion. Unfortunately the converse is also true: some who blossom so brightly and so young, fade quickly.

To sum up, the causes of scholastic failure are many, but not beyond the understanding of any who will take the trouble to make a careful and patient study of the boy or girl in trouble. Laziness, stupidity, and lack of power to concentrate are overworked and poor explanations that usually indicate meager understanding on their user's part. The factors briefly outlined and illustrated here are more likely causes. At times no definite cause can be found but sometimes though none is found, the boy will begin to improve. It could be that just your concern with his future and your interest in him will spur him on to greater effort.

XI

Stealing and Other Anti-Social Behavior

More important than a discussion of what to do about stealing or cheating, or about delinquency, is a consideration of
the reasons behind such behavior. If one is to talk about prevention, it is certainly more profitable to consider the causes
than it is to consider the effect of various types of punishment. What are the characteristics of adolescents which one
has to keep in mind in any effort to solve these problems?

Adolescents are great imitators. A girl who admires her
mother or teacher, club leader or an older girl — a boy who

admires his father, his minister, his teacher, his coach, or his scoutmaster — will imitate their gestures, walk, speech, *and honesty*. But it is difficult to develop honesty in a boy whose father boasts of his tax-evading, ticket-fixing and shady deals, or in a girl whose mother is unreliable and is forever giving false excuses and explanations. There is little use in preaching honesty and practicing deceit. But honesty in adults whom adolescents admire is likely to be imitated.

Not only adults' conduct but also their own contemporaries' behavior strongly affects the adolescent. They do not like going against their group's mores and rules; they fear being different, being an outsider. Bad leadership in such a group can spread like wildfire and play havoc with many boys and girls. Bill, picked up by the police for stealing candy, told a common story: 'I never used to steal. But when we moved I had no friends so I tried to get in with the gang that hangs around our housing project. They all steal. You can't run with them unless you do too. I didn't want the candy. I didn't want to steal, but I didn't want to get kicked out of the gang and have them after me.'

It isn't always 'gang law.' It can be just neighborhood mores. Helen's family were generous to her, she had no excuse for stealing except her 'We all steal from that store. They cheat you. It's the only store handy to school and we all get our notebooks and things like that there. They charge us more than they ought to so we just get back at them whenever we can. They're mean, too.' Her group didn't call this dishonesty. When Helen was caught, it just made them madder than ever at the storekeeper. They thought she had been pretty stupid to be caught.

New rules imposed to correct a bad situation are rarely effective. By nature adolescents resent inroads on their independence, but rules in which they have a part, whether formulated by their family, their school, or their club, they are likely to respect. By participation in the making of rules, their independence has not suffered a setback, and they have an understanding of the reason for these rules. Such rules have two virtues: they are likely to be respected, and the making of them is a valuable experience in cooperative living.

Adolescents do not like to be 'shoved around.' They are striving for independence, they have need of praise as well as censure, they have aggressive impulses for which acceptable outlets must be found. They have a need for success and satisfaction of some sort. If you deny or ignore these traits and needs, all the rules and policemen will not prevent asocial behavior. Because they are younger than adults is a poor reason for telling them, 'Do as I say, don't mind why.' A reasonable explanation is better, but a group conference and then a group decision is best.

A little praise when deserved won't spoil them. Even a successful professional athlete, whom you would think saturated with praise, notices when his home run gets little applause. Little wonder that the adolescent growls, 'Whadda the bastids want?' when his best efforts go unnoticed and his slightest error gets carping criticisim.

Equally futile are rules which deny youths opportunities to give harmless vent to their exuberance and aggression. Athletics are a great outlet. Kicking a soccer ball is much better than breaking windows, and screaming at Saturday movie or game lets off steam which insures a pressure more suitable to next day's church. To berate them for not 'behaving maturely' is to forget the fact that they are not mature. They will become so — and in a healthier fashion — if this simple biological fact is not ignored.

Recognition of their needs and and personalities will do more to prevent their asocial behavior than will rules. Denial of them, a stern imposition of an impatient or frustrated adult's will, can accomplish little more than to make him an unhappy and very busy policeman. But to recognize adolescents' needs does not mean to give them free rein and to let it go at that. Fulfill their *needs*, not their *whims*, and take every opportunity to teach them how rewarding cooperation can be. Taking a part in the making of the school's or club's rules is an invaluable aid to their understanding of the need for law and order.

Adolescents must learn to govern *themselves*. Home and school and clubs which govern them, in which they have little say in lawmaking or administration, may seem to run smoothly but they are at best only preparing young people to be governed. There is little to be said for a method which develops submissive, dependent adults. What is needed is a preparation which gets them ready to govern themselves. Admittedly their first — and even later — efforts at self-government will be awkward and clumsy and inefficient; but they will learn, and they will respond best to those adults who continue to trust them despite their errors. The less adults show authority and impose needless rules, the better they understand young people and their needs and the more freely they allow adolescents to govern themselves and make their own rules, the better the preventive job the adult is doing. It is in this way, not by punishment and endless rules and policing, that asocial behavior is prevented and the spirit of cooperative group living in a democratic society is inculcated.

The prevention of stealing and cheating among adolescents is fundamental, but it is obviously necessary to understand these forms of asocial behavior so that they can be properly managed when they do occur. Stealing is common among little children and it is unlikely that anyone can truly say that he has *never* stolen. Most of us can remember taking something in order to appear generous by giving it to someone we admired, or to make ourselves appear more important by having such a special possession or to replace something lost and thereby avoid punishment. These are but a few of the types of childish thefts. As they grow older, most children satisfy the needs which motivate these thefts in more socially acceptable ways, but a few never really grow up emotionally and continue to steal in adolescence. The stealing of early childhood is neither to be ignored nor punished harshly; it is its persistence as the boy or girl grows older that demands serious attention. Even then a search for the reason for this stealing, not the stealing itself, requires attention. Why is this boy or girl not maturing emotionally, what are the strong inner needs which are unsatisfied and are now demanding satisfaction in this abnormal way?

No infant has a sense of property rights. We expect, and are even amused, by the way a baby grabs everything within his reach, regardless of ownership. He does not feel that he should give anything in return. As he grows older, however, we properly expect him to grow out of these childish ways and to know that taking things which do not belong to him is no longer amusing. Stealing in the adolescent is at times a persistence of this sort of infantile behavior. It will not be cured, or properly managed, unless its origin is understood and the condition which produced it is modified. A boy who was starved for affection in his early years, and who as he grows older finds little acceptance from adults or his contemporaries, may turn to taking things. These *things* may bring him the satisfactions which he has never had from *people*. In a similar way the lonesome boy away from home may take from those who ignore him to give to loved ones he has left behind.

Tom had two older brothers — when he was sixteen they were away at college — and two younger sisters. His father, a busy physician, was rarely home. When he was home, he was often tired and irritable and it seemed as if his daily work had drained his desire or capacity to understand people. Tom's mother kept very busy with what she called her social obligations: teas, bridge, clubs, charities. Less able or energetic than either of them, Tom grew apart from them and spent most of his time with boys of his own age. He had no very close friends but he kept busy and seemed happy. Then suddenly one day his father said he wanted to talk to him. 'I've arranged for you to go to boarding school. It's a good school. They'll teach you to concentrate. Your mother and I are going away for a few months.'

Tom was stunned, and he protested feebly that he'd rather stay on in high school. He was told not to be childish, that this was a great opportunity that any boy would jump at, and that it was all settled anyway. So after the Christmas holidays he found himself away from home, in a new school with new companions, new teachers, and new ways. Everybody else seemed to have friends; no one seemed particularly interested in him. There wasn't much free time — he was glad of that, because he didn't know what to do with himself when there weren't classes or athletics to go to.

He'd never stolen before. But now it wasn't long before he found himself taking things. Little things, big things, things he didn't need. From anyone. Not for spite. Not to use them: he just stored them in his trunk. Finally he was caught. This time it seemed as though he might have wanted to be caught he was so clumsy and careless about it. 'I don't know why I steal. I don't want the stuff. I just do it. I know that sounds silly. I can't seem to stop — I *think* I want to, but I'm not sure.'

This boy's stealing is clearly neurotic behavior. It will not be cured by punishment or by public disgrace. He needs friends, not ostracism; he needs a friendly atmosphere in which to develop emotionally, not the resentment and loneliness of rejection. This attempt to explain his stealing on the basis of his unfulfilled needs does not ignore or condone his stealing. On the contrary it is an effort to *cure* it by finding and eliminating its cause. Punishment, swift or deliberate, harsh or mild, never can be as effective as a successful search for, and then removal of, the underlying needs and tensions which produced the misbehavior; and then, when the cause has been found, an attempt must be made to fulfill those needs and relieve those tensions *in a socially acceptable way*. They can't just be given free rein. The boy or girl has to learn to live in a world which demands some restraint and compromise and an ability to live with regard for others. That they have stolen does not mean that they will never be able to adjust to the reasonable restrictions which civilized community living demands, but rather that temporarily their tensions were overpowering: when they are relieved a healthy and socially acceptable life can be entirely possible. Punishment alone only multiplies their maladjustment and perpetuates their emotional immaturity.

It is, however, unrealistic to assume that all stealing is a manifestation of neuroticism, or evidence of hitherto unappeased normal needs for security and affection which an adolescent is trying to satisfy in this abnormal way. Stealing may at times be on no more subtle basis than that a girl or boy saw something and without further thought took it. Or it may have been deliberately planned at a time of desperate need. It is when the stealing seems stupid, when it doesn't make sense, when things not wanted or needed are stolen, or stolen and destroyed, that one should expect to find an unconscious motivation for his unsocial behavior. There may be unconscious factors in all stealing, but usually it is not difficult to distinguish senseless stealing from that which meets some tangible deprivation or which is a reflection of little or no conscience.

Stealing of things of which an adolescent has clearly been deprived and badly wants sometimes has unconscious elements which should not be ignored. When accompanied by wanton destruction of other articles or violent aggression, unconscious factors which demand attention are undoubtedly at work. Hungry girls or boys will steal bread, but if they smash furniture and stamp on the cakes they leave behind, they are satisfying much more than hunger, and much more than their hunger will have to have attention if they are truly to be rehabilitated.

There is much that is not known, there is much to learn, about stealing. But there is little excuse for swift, harsh punishment that cannot wait for thorough investigation. Adolescents learn not only from their sins and their successes, but from the way adults treat them. They can be given an object lesson in deliberation and in concern for the individual, or they see hasty judgment and a preoccupation with the effect of the individual's act upon the health of the group. Too often an individual's good is subjugated to that of the group: the fact that the group is made up of individuals is apparently forgotten. In these days of mass production and sovietism it is well to give adolescents every opportunity to observe the respect which adults in a democratic society have for each individual.

That little is known about stealing, or that swift 'justice' and thorough study of an individual case are incompatible, are poor reasons for not trying to understand each boy's problem. To study it, to deliberate, is not to condone or to ignore its seriousness. If such tactics accomplish no more than to serve as an example of rational thinking and the regard of one human being for another, much will have been accomplished.

Young people who grow up in a household where there is no adult to whom they feel strongly attached are likely to have little regard for other people or for other people's possessions. They think and behave as though people had never meant very much to them. Janet was like that. Her father had never gotten along very well with her mother, and when war broke out he jumped at the chance to leave home. Janet was five then. Her mother, feeling abandoned, went home to her own mother, whom she had never really left, and let bridge increasingly occupy her time and mind. Janet strongly resembled her father and got little attention from her grandmother. When the war was over, her father did not return. Janet, now ten, was sent to a boarding school. Unfortunately it was a school which had seen better days and now was barely struggling along, its faculty dissatisfied and complaining and its few students tolerated regardless of their misbehavior.

Janet had always stolen — stamps, small change, and pencils from her mother and grandmother, crayons from a local five and ten cent store. She had money but she had never liked to spend it; she had toys but would never let other children play with them. At boarding school she continued to steal; they were mostly little things, and chiefly from her roommate, whose mother came to see her every week and always brought her a present.

When Janet was fourteen, her mother married again and her stepfather showered her with gifts to win her affection. 'I can't stand him; he tries to be nice but he's so spineless — he lets my mother push him around and all he does is buy her things — at least he did until he lost his job — now he doesn't make much money and he can't. I wish she had married someone I could like.'

Janet's stealing was now a real problem. She was too old to excuse, and she stole so frequently that her parents knew she would be caught sooner or later. What they could not seem to understand was that this rejected, affection-starved child had grown into adolescence with little or no relationship to any adults whom she could admire and respect. Her contemporaries she sometimes envied, and always ignored lest they in turn snub her. Resenting those who had ties and affection, deprived herself, and having no warm feeling for any adult, they and their possessions had little meaning for her. To take from them aroused only concealed, unconscious emotion.

Adolescents like Janet can't be won over with gifts, or cured of their stealing with threats. Under like circumstances the oft-repeated 'How can you hurt your mother' is pathetic; and vacillating attempts at discipline and punishment are only futile. A strong emotional tie to someone they respect and like, and firm but kindly management of any subsequent stealing can salvage some of these starved and immature and warped personalities. Their cure as well as their prevention is chiefly in a close association with an adult they can admire and who will show feeling for them as well as interest in their welfare.

The soundest treatment of the adolescent who steals is the one which first attempts to find and cure its cause. Unless boys and girls subsequently understand and conquer the reasons for the misbehavior, they will not have been made ready for their place as adults in a free and civilized society. Patience and a desire to help them will often disclose the causes, and a little ingenuity and kindliness can effect a real cure. Sometimes psychiatric assistance will be necessary, but much can be accomplished by those who have no professional training but do have a real desire to be helpful.

Cheating in school is a subject of never-ending debate. Honor systems are tried and discarded and revived. Rules are made and revised and methods of supervision come and go. But cheating seems to die hard. In some schools cheating is so common that it is rarely condemned by the students themselves. In a few institutions cheating is really taboo and a boy or girl who cheats is ostracized. This is the key to the situation: when *their own group* has made cheating taboo, it is rarely practiced.

Rules and supervisors and teacher-instigated honor systems usually fail. Pupil versus teacher is a traditional contest hard to forget; teachers perpetuate it by their 'trick questions' and 'surprise quizzes.' So there is a thrill in beating the game, particularly since the opponent's position of authority compensates for his being outnumbered and gives the contestants a semblance of being evenly matched! But when a group has drawn up its own rules, and after age has endowed these rules with a mantle of tradition commanding respect, cheating will be at a minimum.

Adolescents dislike change. They are idealists who respect and will strive to maintain a long tradition. Hence the success of the honor system at a few schools and colleges. When it is well established *and supported by the group,* no boy doubts its force or the consequences of any misstep. However, when an honor system is frequently violated, it is no better than other rules or supervision. It is then a game to beat, a game fallen into disrepute, and 'honor system' has become a misnomer. Honor systems achieve respect slowly. Too often they are the product of a teacher committee or a small group of students and the mass does not feel it has participated.

Equally inimical to the development of a respected tradition are scholastic demands which are beyond many students' capacity; assignments which are too long, grading which is too severe, laboratory exercises which few can finish — these students circumvent by copying each other's work and by other ways. Since the demands are considered by most to be unreasonable, this form of cheating is not regarded by the students as dishonest. It is the institution and its methods which need modification in such a case. Surely it is poor education to perpetuate a system which fosters cheating. A good institution will mend its ways when after a careful study of the facts they prove to be at fault.

Honor systems do not need to cling tenaciously to rule-of-thumb dismissals for every infraction of rules. Neither a good system nor a good institution will be destroyed by tempering justice with mercy. Isolated, first offenses under truly extenuating circumstances can be handled with leniency and will strengthen rather than destroy the system. Students are good judges of each other's pressures. They have little difficulty in distinguishing an unlikely story from an overwhelming circumstance.

It is well for young people to have these experiences. They are the sort of things which prepare them for the decisions of adult life. At times they need to be reminded that the true purpose of education is to make men fit for the world, and that at times this can better be accomplished by leniency than by strict adherence to the letter of the law. It is sounder biology to teach cooperation, and the need of making more of us fit to survive, than to preach survival of the fittest.

Exceptions to rules under proper circumstances are certainly wise; but frequently exceptions or rules made for trivial reasons produce a situation which adolescents find uncomfortable and hard to understand. An adolescent wants to know where he stands. He is anxious, tense, and insecure enough anyway; and when rules always give way to exceptions, when policy vacillates between harshness and leniency, impetuosity and deliberation, and when rules are constantly changed, he becomes very confused and very annoyed. When an institution — or parent — constantly changes tactics and rules, the adolescent loses respect, learns nothing about proper behavior, and builds up tension and resentment. So he says, in effect, they don't know what they're doing, I guess I'll suit myself.

Too often in such homes and schools, what adults call 'sudden outbursts' occur. They happen suddenly, but they are the product of long-mounting tension. Adults who are sympathetic to adolescents and understand them rarely incite these outbursts. They don't foster the tensions which produce them.

The parent, teacher, coach, or club leader who is interested in adolescents and their development and is not blinded by isolated misbehavior will solve most of these problems which arise. But if he or she becomes immersed in the fact of stealing or cheating, and is concerned only with *it*, there is little likelihood that either the problem or the adolescent will benefit. 'Stealing must be stamped out,' 'cheating must be stopped,' all will agree, but unfortunately those who shout these the loudest give least heed to the individuals who have offended, and talk vaguely but vociferously about the example set to others. Careful, just action in one instance will do more to defeat the problem and to instruct and mature the group than will swift punishment; and it will avoid the ill effects which rejection and ridicule produce in a young person already emotionally disturbed. Individualized treatment does not mean no punishment for anyone. It does mean that an attempt is made to find and eliminate the cause of the asocial behavior and then to treat the offender so that his or her emotional maturity and social consciousness will be developed.

Opportunities for their participation in group living and in taking group responsibilities are better preventives of asocial behavior in adolescents than are adult-made rules: early efforts to alleviate signs of frustration will do more than to devise new ways to curb them. When they do go astray, rejected, tense adolescents will almost always respond better to kindness than to power, to opportunities to channel aggression than to restriction, to chances to join rather than be excluded from a group. Very few are not worth giving the chance to discover that cooperation yields more happiness than selfishness. The teacher, counselor, club leader, minister, or physician first using these methods will make mistakes, but as skill is gained, the satisfaction of seeing an upset adolescent develop poise and a new-found maturity as a result of such talks will far out-balance one's earlier disappointment.

How do you distinguish the normal adolescent from the delinquent? It is in the matter of conscience that the true delinquent differs most. But among delinquents there are many types, and a variety of degrees of severity. Redl divides delinquents into four groups: the basically healthy adolescent whose behavior is a not unexpected reaction to a bad setting; the sound adolescent whose behavior has grown out of his excessive turmoil — his adolescence is temporarily too much for him; the neurotic delinquent; and the guilt-free, remorse-free, impulsive, true delinquent who has little conscience, little personality strength. Bill, whom we mentioned at the start of this chapter, falls into the first group; there are elements of the second in both Tom and Janet, though each really belongs in the neurotic group — their problems were deeper, less transient. Most of us only infrequently see young people who fall into the fourth category. They are not the most difficult to understand but they are the most difficult to help. They need but cannot accept affection. They need to live in a routine, predictable, orderly way, but they can't accept regimentation. They are impulsive; they overact to frustration with rage and to success with intolerable boasting.

What are the implications for prevention that these stories and these comments offer? Obviously, in any individual a variety of factors are at work when delinquency develops. These may be chiefly related to his or her community, family, or own self — the latter being in no small part the product of heredity.

Stable, friendly communities are best. It isn't by any means just a matter of economics, of how good the housing; it's a matter of how well the community gets along; how much hostility, envy, and inter-group strife there is. If there isn't much of those, the chances are that its young people will have a feeling of belonging — and will be well-adjusted and stable, no matter how poor the housing. But if the atmosphere is rife with struggle for success and with intolerance, big lawns and fine houses or slum areas will each foster delinquency. People who are preoccupied with their own struggle for mastery, who openly hate their neighbors and are intolerant of those of different backgrounds, have little time for their own children; they're impatient, they're busy 'getting ahead.' On the move, their children don't know where they stand. So these young people, abandoned by their parents, develop a world of their own — a world with its own language, laws, and costume: the leather-jacket gangs of today. They are as faithful and loyal to their own group and its laws as they are oblivious to, and regardless of, those of adults.

But even in the most unstable, the most unfriendly communities, delinquency need not always develop and obviously only infrequently does. In such a community a good family, good relationships to his or her parents, save the day. Close ties to good people — and good people at home, at school, in the church, and at the club to imitate — account in great part for the many fine young people whom we find coming out of communities which are blamed for another's downfall.

And in the best or worst of circumstances — community or family — the person himself is a factor. Of what biological stuff is this boy or girl made? Some, the fortunate ones, seem almost indestructible; others are precariously balanced. This we cannot alter, but it is important to remember. Otherwise we will frequently be surprised at how little stress one, and how much adversity another, can withstand.

We should remember, too, that such a thing as conscience needs to be developed. It doesn't just happen. From their early years, when still very little people, boys and girls need to learn increasingly to distinguish right from wrong. This does not mean that they should be bombarded with endless 'No's' and punished and frustrated and inhibited to the point of becoming little automatons. But controls and conscience will be needed in adolescence and they won't be there if the difference between right and wrong isn't taught — and taught consistently, simply, firmly, and kindly from very early childhood. It's parents who vacillate between strictness for its own sake and yielding to every whim, who disagree with one another about what is right or wrong, who write false excuses to the teacher, who play one parent against the other — 'go ahead but don't let your father know' — who read their children's diaries or mail, who never offer corrections 'because the dear little child must express himself,' who think a little child can distinguish between setting a fire in a sink from setting one on a carpet — it's those who don't foster the development of the sort of conscience and controls an adolescent will need.

For our part — all of us — we can encourage and teach the principles of good early training; combat deprivation, poverty, and want; support slum clearance and mental health agencies; encourage the development of stability and tolerance in communities; support Boys' Clubs and other similar community ventures; give young people early and increasing opportunities to participate in their families', their schools', and their clubs' problems and government. If we are to lower the incidence of delinquency in our communities, and we all say we want to, each of us must actively work for all these things. Our success will be in proportion to how real our interest is, how much we really want to get delinquency under control.

And when faced with delinquent behavior, we can try *ourselves*, remembering the causes of asocial behavior and the kind of person involved, to help this boy or girl to find the cure. Sometimes we'll need professional help, sometimes a psychiatrist; but much can, at least at first, be done by those who, though lacking extensive experience or special training, have a real desire to be helpful. By all means call for skillful help when it is needed, but don't let your own low opinion of your competence provide too easy an excuse for reaching for the telephone rather than settling down to do some listening and helping yourself. Your helping hand — your genuine interest — your willingness to give of yourself and your time right at the time of a crisis, may be worth its weight in gold. Remember always that kindliness antedates psychiatry by hundreds of years.

FOR FURTHER READING

Blos, P. *The Adolescent Personality*, New York, 1941, Appleton-Century-Crofts, Inc.

Burgess, E. W., and Fishbein, M., editors. *Successful Marriage*, Garden City, New York, 1955, Doubleday & Co., Inc.

Cole, W. G., *Sex in Christianity and Psychoanalysis*, New York, 1955, Oxford University Press, Inc.

Debesse, M. *L'Adolescence*, Paris, France, 1956, Presses Universitaires de France.

English, O. S., and Pearson, G. H. J. *Emotional Problems of Living*, New York, 1945 (revised 1955), W. W. Norton & Co., Inc.

Erikson, E. *Childhood and Society*, New York, 1950, W. W. Norton & Co., Inc.

Faegre, M. L. *The Adolescent in Your Family*, Washington, D.C., 1955, U.S. Department of Health, Education, and Welfare.

Farnsworth, D. L. *Mental Health in College and University*, Cambridge, Mass., 1957, Harvard University Press.

Fleming, C. M. *Adolescence*, London, 1948, George Routledge, Inc.

Frank, M., and Frank, L. K. *Your Adolescent at Home and in School*, New York, 1956, The Viking Press.

Fry, C. C. *Mental Health in College*, New York, 1942, The Commonwealth Fund.

Gallagher, J. R. *Understanding Your Son's Adolescence*, Boston, 1951, Atlantic, Little Brown & Co.

Gesell, A., Ilg, F. L., and Ames, L. B. *Youth—The Years from Ten to Sixteen*, New York, 1956, Harper & Bros.

Gillingham, A., and Stillman, B. W. *Remedial Training for Children with Specific Disability in Reading, Spelling and Penmanship*, 397 pp. Bronxville, N.Y., privately printed, 1946. (Distributed by Anna Gillingham.)

Glueck, S., and Glueck, E. *Unraveling Juvenile Delinquency*, New York, 1950, The Commonwealth Fund.

Hand, Learned, *The Spirit of Liberty*, New York, 1952, Alfred A. Knopf, Inc.

Kirkendall, L. A. *Understanding Sex*, Chicago, 1947, Science Research Associates.

Kluckholm, C., and Murray, H. A., editors. *Personality in Nature, Society and Culture*, New York, 1949, Alfred A. Knopf, Inc.

Lerrigo, M. C., and Southard, H. *Sex Facts and Attitudes. Parents' Privilege. A Story about You. What's Happening to Me? Learning about Love*. Chicago, 1955, The Dutton Series on Sex Education: American Medical Association.

Menninger, W. C. *Understanding Yourself*, Chicago, 1948, Science Research Associates.

Pearson, G. H. J. *Psychoanalysis and the Education of the Child*, New York, 1954, W. W. Norton & Co., Inc.

Plant, J. S. *The Envelope: A Study of the Impact of the World upon the Child*, New York, 1950, The Commonwealth Fund.

Saul, L. J. *Bases of Human Behavior*, Philadelphia, 1951, J. B. Lippincott Co.

Tanner, J. M. *Growth at Adolescence*, Springfield, Illinois, 1955, Charles C Thomas.

Teicher, J. D. *Your Child and His Problems*, Boston, 1955, Little, Brown and Company.

Williams, Roger J. *The Human Frontier*. New York, Harcourt, Brace & Co., 1946.